THE SCIENCE
OF WEATHER

The following poem appears in recognition
of the considerable debt of gratitude
the author owes to his wife.

Storm

Blow out thy mightiest blasty breath;
Scream out thy fury round my roof;
Pour down thy floods and drown the sky,
But I, within, will stay aloof.
My hearthfire, warm, steadfast and bright
Will keep thy demons from my door
Till they are spent, outwrought, outdone,
And all outside is calm once more.

MARY H. DAY

 ADDISON-WESLEY PUBLISHING COMPANY

JOHN A. DAY

THE
SCIENCE
OF
WEATHER

READING, MASSACHUSETTS · PALO ALTO · LONDON · DON MILLS, ONTARIO

PREFACE

This book has emerged out of a conviction born of three decades of experience—one as a practicing meteorologist and two as a college and university teacher and researcher. The conviction has to do with a knotty educational problem which can be stated as follows: What kind of valid experience in science can be offered to students who do not intend to become science majors?

As one looks over the panorama of curricular requirements and offerings in various schools throughout the country, one sees many kinds of solution. These run from the conventional physical and biological science survey courses to the standard introductory laboratory courses in physics, chemistry, biology, etc. Occasionally one sees more imaginative efforts in the way of integrated course sequences in the various sciences. Very infrequently does one find an offering in meteorology for non-meteorologists which can be taken to satisfy a science requirement.

In my view this is a lamentable omission. For my conviction is that meteorology is a uniquely valuable vehicle through which a non-science major can be exposed to those experiences in science which we wish him to have.

I am now convinced that the primary value to the student of a study of meteorology—the Science of Weather—is its high carryover value. It is a truism that we humans have to live out our "three score and ten" at the bottom of a vast "ocean" of air; our every action is influenced in a variety of ways by changes which occur in the state of this "ocean"—changes in temperature, wind, humidity, precipitation, cloudiness, and/or sunshine. When we attain some understanding of the causes of these changes we enhance our ability to anticipate the changes and plan and act accordingly. We also sense the concept of an orderly pattern in nature (as contrasted to the capriciousness associated with weather in earlier days) and feel more at home in the natural order. In other words, once we have formally studied the subject of meteorology, the knowledge gained thereby is, in one way or another, consciously or unconsciously applied every day thereafter. Few academic subjects have such direct carryover value.

The study of weather is an excellent vehicle through which to teach basic scientific principles in an orderly, integrated way. One can take, for instance, the concept of energy, starting with its release in the fusion events which occur in the depths of the sun, and proceed to establish a chain of connecting links between this beginning and the end result: the clouds one sees and the wind and rain one feels on one's face. In the process it becomes possible to develop and apply the fundamental laws of radiation, heat, and motion. The student is thus brought into contact with the basic elements of physical science, not in isolation, but through their application.

One of the problems faced by those who try to implement views such as these through course offerings in the academic curriculum is the education of one's colleagues to the "new look" in meteorology. In the popular eye the subject still smacks too much of non-science: rain-at-the-weatherman's-picnic sort of thing.

It is necessary that citizens at large, and educators in particular, come to realize that we are at the beginning of a new age as regards man's relation to his environment. This is an age in which increasingly large efforts are being put forth to understand those complexities of the atmosphere-earth-sun system which are the root cause of inaccurate forecasts. This is possible because of exciting new technological developments such as the high-speed digital computer, weather satellites, and weather radar. But even more important than these is the feeling that, having the tools for gaining new understanding, we now are limited only by the human factor.

This factor is comprised of two requirements. One is trained minds motivated to carry on research in atmospheric science. The other is an informed citizenry ready to insist that a fair share of the tax dollar be directed to the support of such research.

One evidence of the spirit of change which is with us in this decade is the action of Congress in reorganizing the sprawling governmental weather services, bringing them all into a new agency called ESSA, the Environmental Science Services Administration.

While it is improbable that any of the needed atmospheric research scientists will be recruited from courses where this book may be used, one would hope that some persons who do come in contact with this book might go out into community life as citizens who have caught a vision of what is being, and can be, accomplished in atmospheric science.

The foregoing does not mean that all forecasts will now be accurate. It does mean that they will become increasingly more accurate. One dramatic example of the improvement in forecast accuracy resulting from the use of the new observing tools is to be found in connection with the hurricane-forecasting services. Man has not yet learned how to change the path or lessen the intensity of this type of tropical storm, though these problems are under theoretical and experimental attack at the present time. However, the surveillance of hurricanes by airplane, radar, and weather satellite is now so effective that there is very little chance that one might sneak into a populated area with inadequate advance notice for residents to evacuate. Hurricane statistics show a dramatic lowering of the human casualty list because of this.

Finally, a word about the organization of the text. We assume no mathematical preparation on the part of the student. We must use technical terms, but these are explained in language any capable high school student should be able to understand. After all, one should not pretend to be able to teach science devoid of scientific terminology. At the request of my students, each chapter has been prefaced by a brief summary statement of the subject matter covered therein.

The first broad subject addressed is that of the observation and distribution of the several weather variables. We then deal with the subject of atmospheric motion, showing how this is the result of an uneven distribution of solar energy received over the surface of the earth. This is followed by a development of the precipitation problem, after which we look at the causes of the major atmospheric severe-storm phenomena—hail, tornadoes, hurricanes, etc. The book concludes with a consideration of the major problems of modern meteorology.

Particular emphasis is given to the precipitation processes, which are explored in detail. The author has come to feel that this aspect of weather is of particular concern to citizens who will be living in an increasingly water-thirsty world.

Any author becomes indebted to many people before a book is brought to completion. In particular I would like to thank the following: those who allowed use of copyrighted material and supplied illustrative plates, members of my 1964 and 1965 classes in meteorology whose critical reactions to the first draft enabled me to improve the finished product, Mary Lou Butchart and Anne Adams for very efficient secretarial assistance, and my wife and family for their patience and understanding.

J. A. D.

September 1965
Linfield College
McMinnville, Oregon

CONTENTS

Clouds   *Clouds are visual manifestations of complex atmospheric processes. Since clouds can be seen, we start this book with a study of these "billboards of the sky." First we look at clouds historically, noting the classification scheme given by Luke Howard. We then present the word description of the ten genera found in the 1956 International Cloud Atlas. Clouds may be analyzed according to four major kinds of vertical motion encountered in nature: orographic, stirring, regular ascent, and convection. After describing these, we conclude the chapter with a brief account of the unusual noctilucent and lenticular cloud types.*

We begin our study of meteorology with the topic of clouds for the simple reason that clouds can be seen. When we observe the sky from an esthetic point of view, we can appreciate the infinite variety made possible by clouds. Colors run the gamut from ominous black through somber gray to pure white. Twice daily the sky takes on brilliant hues of red, orange, and yellow, or delicate pastel shades of pink and rose. But as students of the science of weather we approach the subject with a different purpose and from a different perspective. Our concern is not beauty, but significance.

To the meteorological novice it may not be obvious that clouds are in reality a manifestation of complex physical processes which are taking place in the atmosphere. Because they are just this, clouds could be termed "billboards of the sky." These billboards advertise the coming weather attractions to the trained eye, whereas the untrained eye may read little or no message at all. Therefore one of the objectives in this first chapter is to sharpen up the eye so these billboard messages can be read with an increased degree of comprehension.

In order to do this we shall first approach the subject historically, looking at the origin of the international classification scheme. Next we shall approach it descriptively, saying some things about the several cloud forms; and finally we shall approach it analytically, looking at the processes which bring clouds of various kinds into existence.

HISTORICAL

As we look back in history we find an anomaly. Clouds were apparently given no generally accepted names until the beginning of the 19th century, whereas the constellations of stars are still referred to by the names given them by astronomers of old.

The first published classification of clouds was the work of the French naturalist Lamarck (1802). It seems that he did not set out to classify all possible clouds; he confined himself to distinguishing certain forms which seemed to be the manifestation of general causes. In spite of its value his work made little general impression, even in France. Perhaps this was due to his choice of rather peculiar French names; perhaps it was because the paper was discredited by appearing in the same publication as forecasts which were based upon astrological data (*Annuaire Météorologique*).

One year later an English pharmacist and naturalist named Luke Howard published a cloud classification which, in striking contrast, achieved very great success and is the basis of the present classification.

As a youth Howard had been impressed by the variety of sky forms resulting from the 1783 volcanic explosion of Asama Yama in Japan. His continued interest in clouds led to the preparation of an important paper, "On the Modification of Clouds," which was published in *Tilloch's Philosophical Magazine* in 1803. In the paper Howard suggested a classification scheme which is still used in much the same form as he proposed it. His innovation was the use of Latin, the universal language of the day, for his descriptive terms. He called a sheet cloud *stratus* (Lat. *stratum* "layer"), a heap cloud *cumulus* (Lat. "pile"), a streak cloud *cirrus* (Lat. "hair"), and a rain cloud *nimbus* (Lat. "violent rain").

In 1840 the German meteorologist Kaemtz added *stratocumulus* to Howard's forms, giving a precise definition which is in agreement with modern usage. Renou, director of the observatories at Parc Saint-Maur and Montsouris, gave in his "Instructions météorologiques" (1855) a classification of clouds to which may be ascribed the origin of several names in the present nomenclature: *cirrocumulus, cirrostratus, altocumulus,* and *altostratus*. His example was soon followed by the scientists at the observatory at Upsala, Sweden. He thus introduced clouds of medium height between low clouds and those of the cirrus family and began the development of the idea, established later by Hildebrandsson, which led to the adoption of height as a criterion. To Kaemtz is also due the distinction at different levels between detached and continuous clouds.

In 1879 Hildebrandson, director of Upsala Observatory, was the first to use photography in the study and classification of cloud forms. In his work dealing with the cloud classification used at the observatory, he included an atlas of 16 photographs. In 1887 he and his colleague Abercromby published a classification of clouds in which they attempted to reconcile existing customs while keeping to Howard's scheme. This was done after Abercromby had made two trips around the world to assure himself that the cloud forms were the same in all parts. The first *International Cloud Atlas*, which appeared in 1896, followed these authors' recommendations closely. Its classification became official and came into almost general use in all countries. The first *Atlas* constituted a great advance in that it made cloud observations throughout the world truly comparable with one another.

Two editions of the *International Cloud Atlas* have appeared in this century. The first was produced in 1931, and the second in 1956. While adhering to the general form of classification, each *Atlas* contains a few new definitions and clarifications. Much of the material in this section is taken from the 1956 *Atlas*.

PLATE 1–1
Cirrus. Photo by author.

DESCRIPTIVE

Étages (Levels or Layers)

Surface and aircraft observations have shown that clouds are generally encountered over a range of altitudes varying from sea level to the level of the tropopause (i.e., 60,000 feet in the tropics, 45,000 feet in middle latitudes, and 25,000 feet in polar regions). By convention, the part of the atmosphere in which clouds are usually present has been vertically divided into three "étages": high, middle, and low. Each étage is defined by the range of levels at which clouds of certain genera occur most frequently. These genera are:

(a) cirrus, cirrocumulus, and cirrostratus for the high étage,

(b) altocumulus and altostratus for the middle étage (though altostratus often extends to higher levels),

(c) stratocumulus and stratus for the low étage.

(d) Special cases: nimbostratus is generally found in the middle étage but it usually extends into the other étages; cumulus and cumulonimbus usually have their bases in the low étage but their vertical extent is often so great that their tops may reach into the middle and high étages.

TABLE 1–1.   Approximate heights of étages in different regions

Étages	Polar regions	Temperate regions	Tropical regions
High	3–8 km (10,000–25,000 ft)	5–13 km (16,500–45,000 ft)	6–18 km (20,000–60,000 ft)
Middle	2–4 km (6500–13,000 ft)	2–7 km (6500–23,000 ft)	2–8 km (6500–25,000 ft)
Low	From the earth's surface to 2 km (6500 ft)	From the earth's surface to 2 km (6500 ft)	From the earth's surface to 2 km (6500 ft)

The étages overlap and their limits vary with latitude. The approximate heights of the limits are as listed in Table 1–1.

A detailed description of the ten genera is given below. This is followed by a brief discussion of the cloud's physical constitution.

(1) *Cirrus, Ci (Howard, 1803). Detached clouds in the form of delicate white filaments or white or mostly white patches or narrow bands. These clouds have a fibrous (hairlike) appearance, or a silky sheen, or both.* See Plate 1–1.

PLATE 1–2
Cirrocumulus.
Photo by author.

PLATE 1-3
Cirrostratus with halo.
Photo courtesy ESSA, Weather Bureau.

Cirrus is composed almost exclusively of ice crystals. These crystals are in general very small, a fact which, together with their sparseness, accounts for the transparency of most cirrus clouds.

Dense cirrus patches or cirrus in tufts may nevertheless contain ice crystals large enough to acquire an appreciable terminal velocity, so that trails of considerable vertical extent may form. Sometimes, though not very frequently, the ice crystals in the trails melt into small water droplets; the trails are then grayish, in contrast to their usual white appearance, and may give rise to the formation of a rainbow.

The trails curve irregularly or slant as a result of wind shear and of the variation in size of the constituent particles; consequently, cirrus filaments near the horizon do not appear parallel to it.

Halo phenomena may occur; circular halos almost never show a complete ring, because of the narrowness of the cirrus clouds.

(2) *Cirrocumulus, Cc (Howard, 1803; Renou, 1855). Thin white patch, sheet, or layer of cloud without shading, composed of very small elements in the form of grains, ripples, etc., merged or separate, and more or less regularly arranged; most of the elements have an apparent width of less than one degree.* See Plate 1-2.

Cirrocumulus is composed almost exclusively of ice crystals; strongly supercooled water droplets may occur but are usually replaced rapidly by ice crystals.

A corona or irisation may sometimes be observed.

(3) *Cirrostratus, Cs (Howard, 1803; Renou, 1855). Transparent, whitish cloud veil of fibrous (hairlike) or smooth appearance, totally or partly covering the sky, and generally producing halo phenomena.* See Plate 1-3.

Cirrostratus is composed mainly of ice crystals. The smallness of these crystals, their sparseness, and the fact that cirrostratus has at most only a moderate depth account for the transparency of this cloud through which the outline of the sun is visible, at least when the latter is not too close to the horizon.

In certain types of cirrostratus, some of the ice crystals are large enough to acquire an appreciable terminal velocity, so that trailing filaments are formed, which give these cirrostratus clouds a fibrous appearance.

Halo phenomena are often observed in thin cirrostratus; sometimes the veil of cirrostratus is so thin that a halo is the only indication of it.

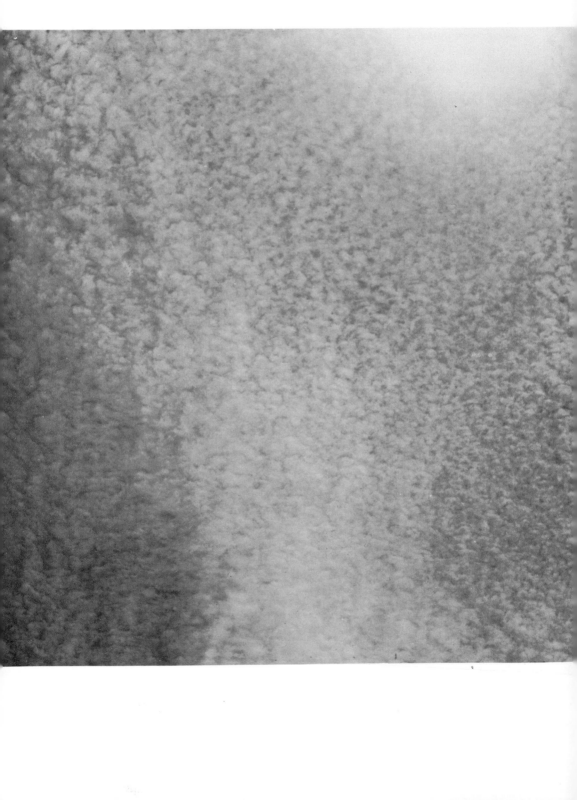

PLATE 1–4
Altocumulus with portion of corona.
Photo by author.

(4) **Altocumulus, Ac** (*Renou, 1870*). *White or gray (or both white and gray) patch, sheet, or layer of cloud, generally with shading, composed of laminae, rounded masses, rolls, etc., which are sometimes partly fibrous or diffuse and which may or may not be merged; most of the regularly arranged small elements usually have an apparent width between one and five degrees.* See Plate 1–4.

Altocumulus is almost invariably composed of water droplets. This is evident from the fairly low transparency of the macroscopic elements and from the fact that the latter show sharp outlines when separate. Nevertheless, when the temperature is very low, ice crystals may form. If the droplets then evaporate, the cloud becomes entirely an ice cloud and its macroscopic elements cease to present sharp outlines. The formation of ice crystals may take place in all species of altocumulus; it occurs most frequently in *altocumulus castellanus* and *floccus*.

A corona or irisation is often observed in thin parts of altocumulus. Parhelia or luminous pillars are sometimes seen in altocumulus, indicating the presence of tabular-shaped ice crystals.

(5) **Altostratus, As** (*Renou, 1877*). *Grayish or bluish sheet or layer of striated, fibrous, or uniform appearance, totally or partly covering the sky, and having parts thin enough to reveal the sun at least vaguely, as through ground glass. Altostratus does not show halo phenomena.* See Plate 1–5.

Altostratus nearly always appears as a layer of great horizontal extent (several tens or hundreds of kilometers, i.e., several thousands of feet). It is composed of water droplets and ice crystals. In its most complete form, three superposed parts may be distinguished, namely:

(a) an upper part composed wholly or mainly of ice crystals,

(b) a middle part composed of a mixture of ice crystals, snow crystals or snowflakes, and supercooled water droplets, and

(c) a lower part composed wholly or mainly of ordinary or supercooled water droplets or drops.

In some cases, the cloud may consist of only two parts, either:

(1) an upper part like (a) and a lower part like (c), or

(2) an upper part like (b) and a lower part like (c).

Less frequently, the entire cloud may be like (a) or (b) alone.

PLATE 1–5
Altostratus. Photo by author.

The constituent particles in the lower part of altostratus are so numerous that the outline of the sun or moon is always dimmed and the surface observer never sees halo phenomena. In the thickest parts, the position of the luminary may be completely concealed.

Raindrops or snowflakes are often present in altostratus and below its base. When precipitation reaches the ground, it is generally of the "continuous" type and in the form of rain, snow, or ice pellets.

(6) Nimbostratus, Ns (CEN,* 1930). Gray cloud layer, often dark, the appearance of which is rendered diffuse by more or less continuously falling rain or snow, which in most cases reaches the ground. It is thick enough throughout to blot out the sun.

high velocity winds accompany

---

* International Commission for the Study of Clouds (CEN) of the International Meteorological Organization (IMO), created in 1921 and dissolved in 1946.

PLATE 1-6
Stratocumulus.
Photo by author.

Low, ragged clouds frequently occur below the layer, with which they may or may not merge.

Nimbostratus is sometimes formed by the spreading out of cumulonimbus (*Ns cumulonimbogenitus*) or, very rarely, when these clouds produce rain, by the spreading out of *cumulus congestus* (*Ns cumulogenitus*).

(7) *Stratocumulus, Sc* (*Kaemtz, 1841*). *Gray or whitish (or both gray and whitish) patch, sheet, or layer of cloud which almost always has dark parts, composed of tessellations, rounded masses, rolls, etc., which are nonfibrous (except for virga) and which may or may not be merged; most of the regularly arranged small elements have an apparent width of more than five degrees. See Plate 1–6.*

cloud reaches to the ground

PLATE 1–7
Stratus. Photo by author.

Stratocumulus is composed of water droplets, sometimes accompanied by raindrops or snow pellets, and more rarely, by snow crystals and snowflakes. Any ice crystals present are usually too sparse to give the cloud a fibrous appearance; during extremely cold weather, however, stratocumulus may produce abundant ice crystal virga which may be accompanied by a halo. When stratocumulus is not very thick, a corona or irisation is sometimes observed.

(8) *Stratus, St (Howard, 1803; Hildebrandsson and Abercromby, 1887). Generally gray cloud layer with a fairly uniform base, which may give drizzle, ice prisms, or snow grains. When the sun is visible through the cloud, its outline is clearly discernible. Stratus does not produce halo phenomena except, possibly, at very low temperatures.* See Plate 1–7.

Sometimes stratus appears in the form of ragged patches.

Stratus is usually composed of small water droplets; this cloud may, when very thin, produce a corona round the sun or moon. At low temperatures, stratus may consist of small ice particles. The ice cloud is usually thin and may on rare occasions produce halo phenomena.

Stratus, when dense or thick, often contains drizzle droplets and some times ice prisms or snow grains; it may then have a dark or even threatening appearance. Stratus with a low optical thickness, when observed at more than 90 degrees from the sun, often shows a more or less smoky, grayish tint like that of fog.

(9) *Cumulus, Cu (Howard, 1803). Detached clouds, generally dense and with sharp outlines, developing vertically in the form of rising mounds, domes, or towers, of which the bulging upper part often resembles a cauliflower. The sunlit parts of these clouds are mostly brilliant white; their base is relatively dark and nearly horizontal.* See Plates 1–8 and 1–9.

Sometimes cumulus is ragged.

Cumulus is distinguished from most altocumulus and stratocumulus by the fact that cumulus clouds are detached and dome-shaped. When viewed from a distance, cumulus clouds may appear merged, as a result of the effect of perspective; in this case, they should not be confused with altocumulus or stratocumulus.

Cumulus tops may spread and form *altocumulus cumulogenitus* or *stratocumulus cumulogenitus.* They may also enter or transpierce pre-existing layers of altocumulus or stratocumulus, or they may merge with

PLATE 1-8
Cumulus of fair weather.
Photo courtesy ESSA, Weather Bureau.

altostratus or nimbostratus. In all such cases, the appellation cumulus should be used so long as the cumuliform clouds remain detached from one another, or so long as they show a considerable vertical extent.

When a very large precipitating cumulus cloud is directly above the observer, it may be confused with altostratus or nimbostratus. The character of the precipitation may then help in distinguishing cumulus from the latter clouds; if the precipitation is of the showery type, the cloud is cumulus.

Since cumulonimbus in general results from the development and transformation of cumulus, it is sometimes difficult to distinguish cumulus with a great vertical extent from cumulonimbus. The cloud should be named cumulus so long as the sprouting upper parts are everywhere sharply defined and no fibrous or striated texture is apparent. If it is not possible to decide on the basis of other criteria whether a cloud is to be named cumulus or cumulonimbus, it should by convention be called cumulus if it is not accompanied by lightning, thunder, or hail.

Cumulus fractus is distinguished from *stratus fractus* by its generally greater vertical extent and its usually whiter and less transparent appearance. Cumulus fractus, furthermore, sometimes has rounded or dome-shaped tops, which are always lacking in stratus fractus.

Cumulus is composed mainly of water droplets. When of great vertical extent, cumulus may release precipitation in the form of rain showers.

Ice crystals may form in those parts of a cumulus in which the temperature is well below 0°C; they grow at the expense of evaporating supercooled water droplets, thereby transforming the cloud into cumulonimbus. In cold weather, when the temperature in the entire cloud is well below 0°C (32°F), this process leads to the degeneration of the cloud into diffuse trails of snow.

(10) **Cumulonimbus, Cb** (*Weilbach, 1880*). *Heavy and dense cloud, with a considerable vertical extent, in the form of a mountain or huge towers. At least part of its upper portion is usually smooth, or fibrous, or striated, and nearly always flattened; this part often spreads out in the shape of an anvil or vast plume.* See Plate 1–10.

Under the base of this cloud, which is often very dark, there are frequently low ragged clouds either merged with it or not, and precipitation sometimes in the form of virga.

Cumulonimbus is composed of water droplets and, especially in its upper portion, of ice crystals. It also contains large raindrops and often snowflakes, snow pellets, ice pellets, or hailstones. The water droplets and raindrops may be substantially supercooled.

PLATE 1–9
Cumulus congestus.
Photo by author.

"nimbus" — erratic

PLATE 1–10
Cumulonimbus. This fully developed
thunderhead was photographed from
an altitude of 30,000 ft; cloud tops
extended to over 45,000 ft.
Photo courtesy U.S. Air Force.

100 Kilo = .621t

TABLE 1–2. Principal classes of clouds according to cause of formation.

Kind of vertical motion	Typical vertical speed, cm/sec	Kind of cloud	Name in international cloud classification
Orographic disturbance	10^2–10^3 *1000 Ki lo. or*	Lenticular or wave cloud – *"pendant"*	Species 'lenticularis'
Widespread irregular stirring	*low* 1–10	Low level, shallow layer clouds, fog	Stratus, stratocumulus *# Nimbostratus*
Widespread regular ascent	*fairly low* 5–20	Multilayer clouds, (continuous in precipitation) *not necessarily true - often there is none*	Cirrus, cirrostratus, altostratus, altocumulus, *✳* nimbostratus
Local penetrative convection	100–500 300–2000	Cumuliform	Cumulus Cumulonimbus

Cumalolamatus – base of cumulo nimbus

ANALYTIC

This brings us to the analytic section of the chapter. Two questions can be posed. First, what circumstances bring about the formation of clouds? Second, what particular circumstances produce the different specific kinds (genera) of clouds?

Since we plan to deal with the physical causes of clouds in some detail in a later chapter, we will attempt only a sketchy answer to these questions at this point.

Air contains water in gaseous form which we refer to as water vapor. Warm air can hold more water vapor than cold air. Air which holds all the water vapor it can hold at a certain temperature is said to be saturated. Air may be brought to saturation in one of two ways: (a) more water vapor may be added to that already present in the air, the air temperature remaining constant, or (b) the temperature of the air may be reduced to the level at which the amount of water vapor present is the

From B. J. Mason, *The Physics of Clouds*, Oxford University Press, 1957.

Typical horizontal extent, km	Typical thickness, km	Typical life of particles, min	Typical kind of precipitation
10 (occasionally 100)	1 (occasionally 10)	10 (occasionally 100)	Nil, occasional intensification of existing precipitation
10^2–10^3	Less than 1	About 100	Nil, or slight snow, or drizzle
10^3	Individually 1, in precipitation 10	Up to 1000	Prolonged moderate snow or rain
1	1	10	Nil, showers of rain,
10	10	20	snow, hail (thunderstorm)

maximum amount the air can hold. In either case, any water vapor in excess of the amount held in the air at saturation changes from a gas to a liquid, the gas molecules gathering together to become tiny droplets. And a cloud is thereby formed.

By far the vast majority of clouds result from the second process: cooling. This leads to another question: How does cooling take place? Once again there are several methods which will be described in greater detail in later chapters. Suffice it now to say that the most effective cooling process is that which results from expansion as air rises to higher elevations and lower atmospheric pressures.

Table 1–2 summarizes the four major kinds of vertical motion encountered in nature, and various characteristics (kind of vertical motion, typical vertical speed, typical horizontal extent, etc.) of the resulting cloud forms. We will discuss each kind in turn.

PLATE 1–11
Sierra wave cloud near
Bishop, California corresponding
to Fig. 1–1. Photo courtesy
U.S. Air Force.

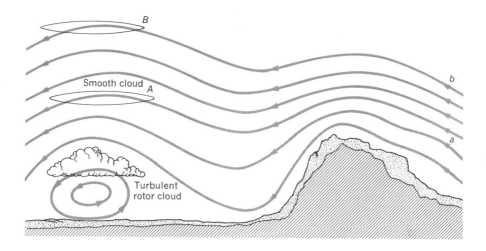

FIG. 1–1
The formation of *lenticularis* standing clouds in the lee of a mountain.

Orographic Disturbances

Since the earth's land surface is irregular in form, surface air must flow
up and down over the features of the land— hills, plains, mountains, and
valleys. Air at higher elevations likewise feels the effect of the surface
features. Air which rises over a geographic barrier undergoes *orographic
lifting*. Depending on the distribution of water vapor within the larger
volume of air, the cooling produced by this lifting may bring certain
layers to saturation. Figure 1–1 shows a situation in which levels A and
B are the saturation (and condensation) levels of small parcels of air at
a and b. Under these circumstances wave clouds are formed in the lee of
the obstruction, and remain stationary as air flows through them, rising
to the saturation level and sinking below it. A very turbulent "rotor
cloud" is formed in the lee. This situation is often encountered in the
lee of the Sierra Nevada range near Bishop, California (Plate 1–11).

If the air were more moisture-laden (as shown in Fig. 1–2 by the
lowering of levels A, B, and C), a thick mass of cloud would be formed
on the windward side of the barrier.

A different set of circumstances is sometimes encountered in the western plains regions, where there is a large land mass sloping gently up
from the Mississippi to the high plains at the base of the Rocky Mountains. If air is forced to ascend this slope, the expansional cooling is
sometimes sufficient to bring the air to saturation. When this occurs, a
large expanse of stratus cloud is formed, which lies on the ground. This
fog tends to be persistent and widespread, and is a hazard to aviation.

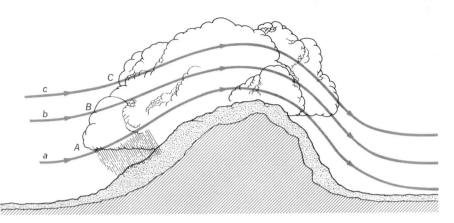

FIG. 1–2
An orographic cloud builds up on the windward side of an obstacle. Precipitation on the windward side removes water from the air; hence, the condensation level is higher on the lee side. (Note that wind direction is opposite to that in Fig. 1–1.)

Stirring

As a result of motion of the air over the surface of the earth, irregular horizontal and vertical eddy motions are induced in the lower layers. This widespread *irregular stirring* tends to bring certain portions of air to saturation, with the resultant production of stratocumulus or stratus cloud forms, depending on local circumstances.

Regular Ascent

Of major interest and concern to meteorologists are those atmospheric systems which by their dynamic nature bring about *widespread* and *regular ascent* of air. One of these is the high-latitude extratropical wave cyclone or depression. Another is the low-latitude tropical cyclone known as hurricane and typhoon. Each of these produces clouds at all levels, and gives rise to patterns of widespread precipitation. For instance, an observer on one of the weather ships stationed (hypothetically) at latitude 45° N in the eastern Pacific Ocean might see the following cloud sequence as a storm system approached and passed. Into initially clear skies, hooked cirrus would first start to rise from the western horizon and would soon be overhead. Gradually the isolated cirrus streaks would thicken into a veil of cirrostratus covering the sky. In a few hours the leading edge of the first sheets of middle clouds (perhaps altocumulus mixed with altostratus) would become visible in the western sky. As this sheet of cloud advanced to cover the whole sky, the sun would be seen only dimly, as if it were shining through a piece of ground glass. The altostratus would soon thicken and become a grey blanket, opaque to the sun. Thickening low clouds would soon develop and gradually merge with the lowering altostratus. About this time precipitation would begin to fall from the low altostratus, and later from the nimbostratus. Accompanying these clouds would be a falling barometer and increasingly strong southerly winds. After several hours of steady but increasingly heavy rain, breaks would appear to the west in the cloud mass as the precipitation became showery and then ceased. The "glass" would start to rise. The wind would shift to the west and then to the northwest. The clouds would change from cumulonimbus to cumuli of diminishing activity and the storm would then have passed on to the east.

Convection

Sometimes the vertical motion in the air is localized and consists of sharp upward thrusts compensated for by larger regions of sinking air. This is *local penetrative convection.* Table 1–2 reminds us of the scale (1 kilometer / 1 kilometer for cumuli, and 10 kilometers / 10 kilometers for cumulonimbi) of horizontal to vertical extent.

A balloon rises when the air within its bag is warmer than that on the outside because of the buoyant forces acting on it. Similarly, a "bubble" of air will rise if its temperature is higher than that of the surrounding

15,000 ft

10,000

5,000

FIG. 1–3
Three stages in the cumulus family. From left to right: cumulus of fair weather, swelling cumulus, cumulonimbus.

PLATE 1–12
This lenticular altocumulus cloud was photographed from the 8000-ft level
on the north slope of Mt. St. Helens, Washington, on May 21, 1950.
The 9677-ft peak is behind the photographer, while a wreath of high
stratocumulus clouds swirls past the summit just above the observer's
level in the 60-knot southwest wind. Lower clouds cover the valley.
Photo courtesy Mrs. Jeanne Cortright Neff.

air. Bubbles of rising air will produce flat-based cumulus clouds. The bases are flat because all the rising air reaches saturation at the same height, or after it has been cooled the same number of degrees.

When the upward thrust of relatively warm air is gentle, the resulting cumuli are shallow. These are the cumuli of fair weather which resemble sheep and lambs peacefully grazing at pasture.

Fair-weather cumuli are characteristic of the trade-wind circulation over the tropical oceans. Each individual cloud has a lifetime of about half an hour. Within a large population of clouds one finds varying stages of birth, growth, decay, and death, as in a population of human beings. As the trade winds approach the western end of the ocean basin they move over a progressively warmer ocean surface. As eddy motion extracts more heat from the surface, the vertical upthrusts of warm air become more vigorous and the depth of the cumuli grows. The result is the cumulus congestus type, which is characterized by hard cauliflower tops.

Sometimes the vertical upthrust pushes up into the atmosphere with explosive violence. As the top of the growing cumulus cloud penetrates well above the freezing level it tends to glaciate; i.e., portions of the cloud undergo a transformation to ice crystals. The external appearance thereby changes from the hard cauliflower head to a stringy, often anvil, shape. The result is the cumulonimbus, an awesome cloud which may produce thunder and lightning, and hail. More will be said about this in the chapter discussing thunderstorms. These three cases are shown in Fig. 1–3.

Some clouds are so unusual that they deserve special mention. One of the mysteries of the cloud world has been that of the *noctilucent cloud,* a cloud form found at altitudes of about fifty miles, or 250,000 feet, in northern latitudes. These clouds are visible at night because sunlight reaching them from far below the horizon is reflected from them to the observer. The mystery has been that there is no evidence of adequate water vapor for cloud formation at such elevations. Scientists at the Air Force Cambridge Research Laboratories have determined that these clouds are composed of meteoric particles. Examination of the samples collected by a specially designed rocket nose-cone shot through the clouds showed that about 20 percent of the microscopic particles were ringed by a halolike structure of undetermined nature. A further unresolved mystery associated with these clouds is why they are seen most often and most vividly in far northern latitudes.

Another group of unusual clouds is typified by the famous "flying saucer" or "grindstone" cloud shown in Plate 1–12. This particular cloud is an outstandingly symmetrical example of the category *altocumulus lenticularis.* Winds which are driven over mountain barriers frequently develop standing wave patterns on the lee side of the barrier. As explained in Fig. 1–1 the cooling which results from the vertical motion is sometimes sufficient to cause condensation at the peaks of the waves. Analysis of the regions from which such clouds are reported shows that, in general, they lie to the east and in the lee of high mountain ranges in the western United States. A further point of interest is that these areas of occurrence partially overlap those areas from which "flying saucers" are most frequently reported.

CHAPTER 2

Weather Variables and Their Measurement

Adequate and accurate description of the atmosphere is the prerequisite to weather prediction. Great masses of information must be shared with interested persons. Weather codes provide the mechanism for this by compressing the maximum information into the minimum space. The international five-digit weather code for surface observations is described and illustrated. Upper-air observations are an equally important part of the description of the atmosphere. After an account of the historical background of man's attempts to measure the state of the upper air, we describe modern systems: Raob, transosonde, weather satellite, and meteorological rocket. Since the problem of measuring the water-vapor content of the air is of unique importance, we deal with it separately and describe the four principal water-measuring devices: hair hygrometer, wet-and-dry-bulb psychrometer, electrical-resistance hygrometer, and dew-point hygrometer.

There seems to be a universal desire, which transcends national and political boundaries, to know precisely what the weather will be at some time in the future. Thus the primary reason for trying to describe accurately the present state of the atmosphere is to enable us to make weather predictions.

Realizing the importance of observations, the meteorologist describes the state of the atmosphere in terms of certain variables which are significantly related to weather change. Improved techniques for making these observations continue to be developed by specialists in meteorological instrumentation.

Primary meteorological questions are: How is the weight of the atmosphere distributed over the surface of the globe and aloft, and how is the distribution changing with time? What is the relative distribution of heat over the surface of the globe and aloft? What are the horizontal and vertical distributions of water vapor? What are the horizontal and vertical components of motion of the atmosphere?

Secondary questions deal with the kind and distribution of cloudiness and precipitation, impediments to visibility, thunder and lightning, ozone content, percentage of sunlight, infrared radiation, concentration of freezing nuclei and cloud nuclei, and so on.

SURFACE OBSERVATIONS

Weather Code for Synoptic Observations

For the purpose of predicting the weather, each nation has established its own network of weather-observation stations. Agreement has been reached through international conferences as to the kinds of observations which must be made, the times at which they will be made, the form in which they will be made and encoded, and the way in which they will be shared with other interested parties. When one tries to visualize weather observers from all over the world going to their weather instruments at the same (Greenwich) hour four times daily, recording the values of wind, pressure, temperature, and moisture, encoding these values in the compact five-digit numerical international weather code for transmission, and sending the message off to a central distribution station for redistribution by radio to all parts of the world—when one tries to visualize all this activity, one is confronted by an inspiring example of intricate organization and magnificent cooperation.

It is not our main purpose to become expert weather observers, so we do not have to master the intricacies of the international weather code.

However, there is virtue in seeing its main features. In its cryptic, symbolic form it is written as follows:

iii Nddff VVwwW PPPTT N_hC_LhC_MC_H T_dT_dapp 7RRR_ts

Sample message:

405   83220   12716   24702   67292   01228   74542

The meaning of the letter symbols is as follows for this sample observation (complete tables are available from the U.S. Weather Bureau):

iii	Station number: 405 is Washington, D.C.
N	Total amount of cloud: 8 means that the sky is covered completely.
dd	True direction from which the wind is blowing: 32 means 320°, i.e., from the NW.
ff	Wind speed in knots: 20 means 20 knots.
VV	Visibility in miles and fractions: 12 means $1\frac{2}{16}$ or $\frac{3}{4}$ mi.
ww	Present weather: 71 means continuous slight snow.
W	Past weather: 6 means rain.
PPP	Barometric pressure in millibars reduced to sea level: 247 means 1024.7 mb.
TT	Current air temperature in degrees celsius (C): 02 means 2°C.
N_h	Fraction of sky covered by low or middle cloud: 6 means $\frac{7}{10}$ or $\frac{8}{10}$.
C_L	Low cloud type: 7 means fractostratus and/or fractocumulus of bad weather.
h	Height of base of cloud: 2 means 300–599 ft.
C_M	Middle cloud type: 9 means altocumulus of chaotic sky.
C_H	High cloud type: 2 means dense cirrus in patches.
T_dT_d	Temperature of the dew point: 01 means 1°C.
a	Characteristic of barograph trace: 2 means rising steadily or unsteadily.
pp	Pressure change in 3 hr preceding observation: 28 means 2.8 mb.
7	Group indicator figure (not plotted).
RR	Amount of precipitation: 45 means 0.45 in.
R_t	Time precipitation began or ended: 4 means 3 to 4 hr ago.
s	Depth of snow on ground (not plotted): 2 means 2 in.

All weather observations are plotted around a small circle centered on the appropriate location. The symbolic station model and the actual message from Washington, D.C. are shown in Fig. 2–1.

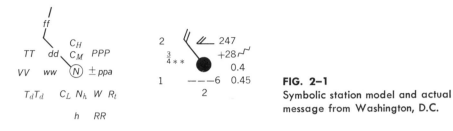

FIG. 2–1
Symbolic station model and actual message from Washington, D.C.

In Fig. 2–2, the weather instruments have been added to show the reader in schematic form the distribution of the several weather variables about the station circle. The meteorologist becomes so familiar with this method of data presentation that, as his eye scans a plotted weather map, he can visualize what is happening throughout the country, much as though he were looking through a series of colored photographs of the clouds and instruments taken at the same time at each of the stations.

The principal observations taken at each ground station are now listed with an accompanying brief description.

Wind Force and Direction

Wind force is measured with an *anemometer,* which is essentially a speedometer. The type illustrated consists of a rotor with hemispherical cups attached to the ends of the spokes. The rotor is exposed atop a pole, where the wind is caught in the cups and causes them to turn at a speed proportional to that of the wind. Indications of the rotor's speed are transmitted electrically to an indicator located, perhaps, inside the weather office. The direction of the wind is indicated by the *wind vane.* The action of the wind on the vane causes it to point into the wind. Wind direction is reported as the direction *from which* the wind is blowing. Thus a vane pointing *toward* the northwest indicates a northwest wind. Indications of the vane's position are transmitted electrically to an indicator inside the office.

Barometric Pressure

This is measured with a barometer such as the mercurial type illustrated. This measurement, expressed in millibars, is the weight per unit area of the air above the station. When the station is not at sea level, this pressure measurement is corrected by an amount equal to the weight of a fictitious column of air between the station and sea level.

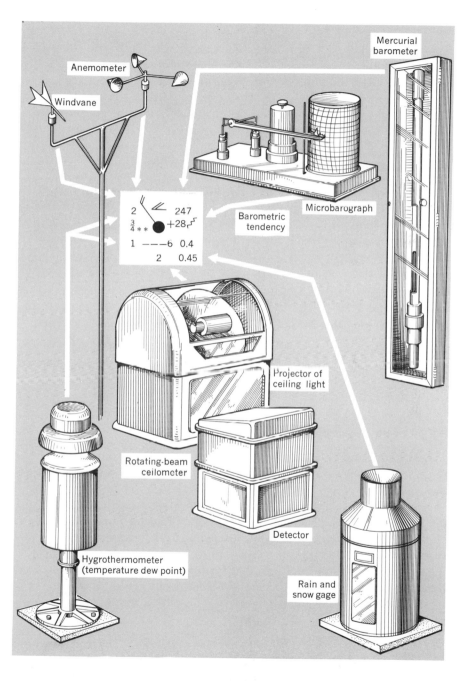

FIG. 2–2
Instruments used in surface-weather observations.
After U.S. Weather Bureau.

Barometric Tendency

This is recorded as a continuous line on the clock-driven chart of a microbarograph. The tendency is the slope of this line taken over the three hours preceding observation. The movement of large masses of air over a given location causes the pressure exerted by the atmosphere to vary constantly. Forecasters look at the fluctuations of pressure for a clue to the movement and intensity of storms.

Amount of Precipitation

This is usually determined from the accumulation caught in a rain gage. In the recording gage of the type illustrated, the weight of the precipitation falling through the 8-inch circular opening of the gage is recorded on a chart as depth of water in inches and hundredths. If 13 ounces of rain were caught in the gage, the recording pen would indicate that 0.45 inch of rain had fallen. The time of the occurrence, as well as the amount of precipitation, can be determined from the chart.

Depth of Snow on the Ground

This is measured to the nearest inch. The measurement is the average of the depth measured at several spots where the snow is least affected by drifting. It includes the depth of all frozen precipitation present—snow, sleet, glaze, hail, and sheet ice.

Height of the Cloud Base

This is determined periodically by a rotating beam ceilometer. As indicated in the diagram, a beam of light from the projector is rotated continuously in a vertical plane and is modulated in order to make the light identifiable to the detector. The field of view of the detector is toward the zenith, and as the beam of light from the projector intersects the base of the cloud, a part of the reflected light is received by the detector. In turn, the detector transmits a signal to the indicator. The indicator, synchronized with the rotation of the projector, translates the received signal into an indication of the actual height of the cloud. If a ceilometer is not available, the cloud base is determined by a small ceiling balloon or by eye observation.

Temperature and Dew Point

The hygrothermometer system is designed for indicating the dew point and free-air temperature through the use of remote-registering thermometers. The dew-point thermometer is encased in a lithium chloride cell which is maintained at the lithium chloride dew point of the ambient air by means of an automatic heating arrangement. Thermometers employed may be of the three-lead resistance type or the liquid-filled type. Slave hands on the temperature indicator provide a means of obtaining the maximum and minimum temperatures. (We will discuss the measurement of moisture more completely in a later section.)

UPPER-AIR OBSERVATIONS

Weather observations taken at the surface of the ground, while necessary, are insufficient. The atmosphere is three-dimensional, and for accurate forecasting the meteorologist absolutely requires a three-dimensional pattern of temperature, pressure, relative humidity, and (if possible) wind.

Kites

During the latter part of the 19th century and the first quarter of the 20th, upper-air information was obtained mainly by sending meteorographs aloft on kites to record automatically on a single sheet the measurements of two or more of the three meteorological elements. This system had several weaknesses:

1. The average altitude reached was only about 10,000 feet, although some flights reached nearly 20,000 feet.
2. The data could not be evaluated until after the observation was completed and the kite and meteorograph were brought back to the ground.
3. Kites could be flown only in good weather and when the winds were neither too light nor too strong.*
4. There was also danger of the kite breaking away and the meteorograph endangering lives and property.

Airplane Observations (Apobs)

From 1925 to 1937, upper-air data were obtained by attaching meteorographs to airplanes (Apobs). While planes continued to be used for this purpose until 1943, their use was greatly curtailed after radiosonde

---

* In 1895 Professor Rotch of the U.S. Blue Hills Observatory obtained measurements up to 8000 feet. This achievement encouraged the U.S. Weather Bureau to organize a kite-flying network of 17 stations, for a 5000-foot-level synoptic coverage. However, the experiment failed because of problems of launching the kites in the light summer winds.

observations were inaugurated. Apobs also had several weaknesses:

1. The average altitude was approximately 17,000 feet and the maximum about 20,000 feet.

2. Data could not be evaluated until the observation was completed and the plane had landed.

3. Observations could not be taken in stormy weather because of lack of blind-landing equipment.

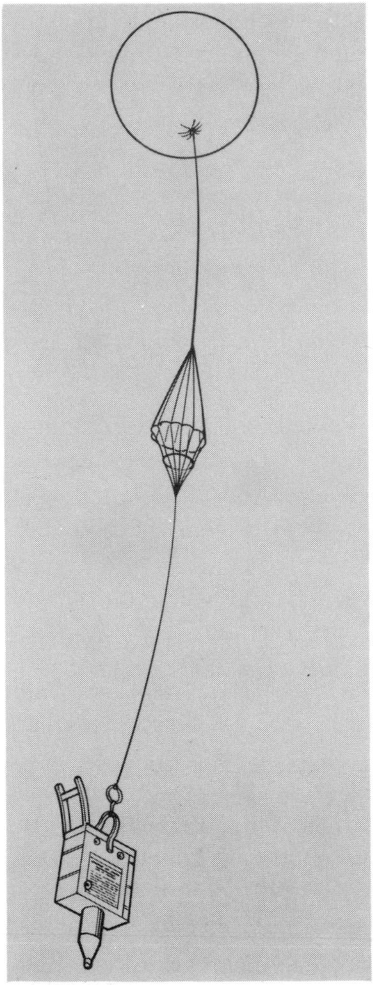

FIG. 2–3
Raob assembly.

Radiosonde Observations (Raobs)

Radiosonde observations, which are radio soundings of the upper air, were inaugurated in 1937. These observations, which can be taken regardless of the weather, do not have many of the weaknesses of the previous systems. The radiosonde consists of pressure-, temperature-, and humidity-sending (i.e., -measuring) elements coupled to a radio transmitter and assembled in a lightweight box. This instrument is carried aloft by a balloon filled with helium (or hydrogen) gas. See Fig. 2–3.

As the balloon carries the radiosonde aloft, values for the temperature, pressure, and relative humidity are transmitted to a ground receiving set where the data are printed out on a recorder chart. Consequently, the data can be evaluated as the observation progresses. The data are recorded in terms of audio-frequencies and must be converted to actual values before being plotted on an adiabatic chart (the meteorologist's working diagram).

When the balloon reaches its elastic limit and bursts, a small parachute slows the descent of the radiosonde, thereby minimizing the danger of injury to lives and damage to property.

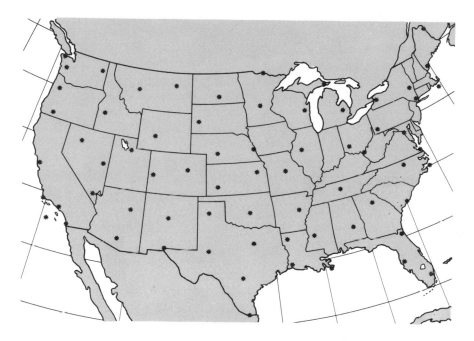

FIG. 2–4
Schematic of Raob net
in the 48 states.

The evaluated data are transmitted over a national teletypewriter system in coded form. When this has been done, they are relayed via various communication systems to all parts of the world for operational use. The data are also entered on punched cards for use in climatology and research projects.

Radiosonde observations are taken either two or four times daily at 96 Weather Bureau stations in the United States and on Caribbean and Pacific islands; and at 43 additional cooperative stations at various points in the Western Hemisphere, including the Caribbean area, the Atlantic and Pacific Oceans, and South America and Mexico. The network in the 48 states is shown in Fig. 2–4. Included in the list of cooperative stations are several ocean-vessel stations in the Atlantic and two in the Pacific. The Coast Guard operates the vessels, while the Weather Bureau provides the meteorological personnel and equipment. These vessels occupy the ocean stations for approximately 21 days at a time, after which they are relieved by other vessels. In addition the Weather Bureau takes radiosonde observations aboard a few ocean liners in the Pacific, the Gulf of Mexico, and the Atlantic.

The altitude reached by radiosonde observations varies for several reasons; e.g., bursting height of the balloon, faulty receiving equipment, or atmospheric interference. Those observations that reach the bursting altitude of the regular 600-gram balloon attain an average height in excess of 90,000 feet. The average bursting altitude for stations now using the larger 1200-gram balloon exceeds 100,000 feet. The average altitude reached for all observations is approximately 75,000 feet, while a number of observations have extended to 125,000 feet, or more.*

Rawinsonde

By direction-finding on the radiosonde signal, the direction and speed of the winds can be determined for the various layers through which the radiosonde passes. The observation is then termed a rawinsonde. All Weather Bureau Raob stations take rawinsondes.

Transosonde

An interesting and valuable application of balloon technology to the gathering of meteorological data is the transosonde. Here we have a full meteorological station borne aloft by a large (40–50 foot) balloon which is so controlled that it will float along a given pressure surface for several days. Because of its meteorological significance the 300-millibar surface is often chosen (this approximates 30,000 feet in elevation). At

---

* The Weather Bureau uses over half a million balloons annually in its program of measuring upper-air pressure, temperature, humidity, and cloud height. Thirty percent are small balloons, called ceiling balloons, which are used to measure cloud height. Fifty percent are somewhat larger pilot balloons, used to determine the direction and speed of the wind at the various levels through which the balloon passes. The remaining twenty percent are used to carry aloft the radiosonde equipment just described. Before World War II the balloons were made of natural rubber latex. When this supply was cut off, a synthetic rubber called *neoprene* was developed and used in the manufacture of balloons. The film thickness of the 600-gram balloons is between 0.002 and 0.004 inch when the balloon is inflated and ready for release. At high bursting altitude this thickness decreases to less than 0.0001 inch.

In the United States, balloons are inflated almost exclusively with helium gas, because of its safety factor. The greatly increased use of helium for other purposes threatens to deplete the United States' supply in the distant future. For this reason it will be necessary to use hydrogen more extensively; the transition from helium to hydrogen is, in fact, now taking place. Hydrogen provides slightly more lift than helium, but it is explosive and must be used with great care.

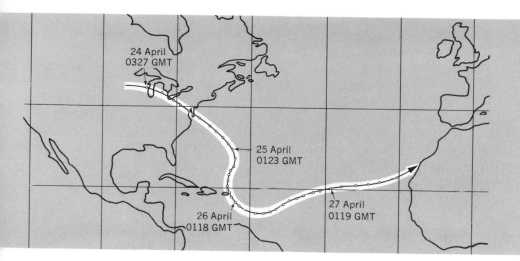

FIG. 2–5
Transosonde flight no. 990 at 300 mb.
Note the mid-Atlantic trough near April 26 position.

intervals the balloon position is determined by radio direction-finding
techniques, and the meteorological information is relayed back to the
ground station in coded transmission similar to that used in the Raob
program. Since the balloon moves with the wind, its successive position
makes it possible to calculate the field of motion. Figure 2–5 shows the
track followed by one of the transosonde flights.

Weather Satellites

One of the most exciting, daring, and imaginative pieces of meteorological planning came to fruition on April 1, 1960. On that date Tiros I, the
first in a distinguished family of weather satellites, was launched into
orbit. This date marks the inauguration of regular observations of clouds
and outgoing infrared radiation, looking *down from the top* of the ocean
of air.

Ten preliminary Tiros satellites have successfully been put into orbit.
Though each has been experimental in nature, leading up to the TOS
(Tiros Operational Satellite) system inaugurated in 1966, each has provided many useful data. Something of the order of half a million cloud
pictures have been taken over the five-year span. The first photomosaic
of the entire world's cloud cover, provided by 450 pictures taken by
Tiros IX on February 13, 1965, is shown in Plate 2–1.

Tiros is the acronym for Television and Infra Red Observation Satellite. All of the Tiros satellites have the same external appearance: each is an 18-sided polygon, 42 inches in diameter and 19 inches high. Sides and top are covered with 9100 n-on-p solar cells and cadmium nickel batteries, the primary power source. The weight of a Tiros is approximately 300 pounds.

Tiros satellites are launched into a nearly circular orbit at a mean altitude of about 450 statute miles. The period of revolution of the satellite about the earth is about 100 minutes.

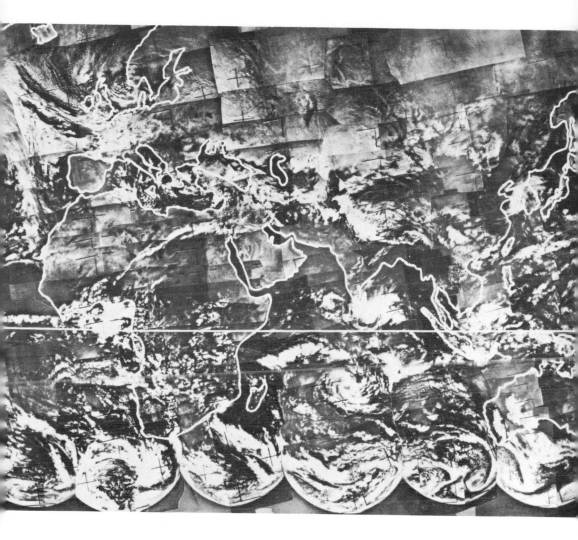

PLATE 2–1
This global photomosaic was assembled from 450 individual photos
taken by Tiros IX during the 24 hours of February 13, 1965.
The horizontal white line marks the equator. Special photographic
processing was used to increase the contrast between major land areas,
outlined in white, and the surrounding oceans. The brightest features
on the photographs are clouds; ice in the Antarctic and snow in the
north are also very bright. The clouds are associated with many
different types of weather patterns. The scalloping at the bottom
shows how the earth's horizon appears in individual pictures.
Photo courtesy ESSA.

The plane of the orbit of the early Tiros satellites launched from Cape Kennedy was inclined about 48 degrees to the equator. Because of this inclination, useful data could not be obtained poleward of approximately 55 degrees latitude. As expertise increased this difficulty was overcome. Tiros IX, launched from the Cape on January 22, 1965, was the first attempt to reach polar orbit from this point. This was accomplished by a series of three dog-leg maneuvers of the Delta launch vehicle which successfully put the satellite in the planned sun-synchronous 83-degree retrograde orbit.

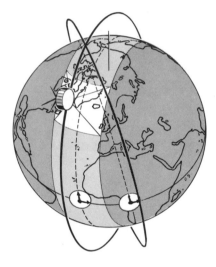

FIG. 2–6
TOS system. Satellite crosses the equator at the same local time each orbit. Each orbit takes 113.5 min; 12.75 orbits are made per day. After photo supplied courtesy of ESSA.

Tiros IX was the first satellite to test the "cartwheel" configuration of the TOS system. Here the satellite's spin axis is initially in the orbital plane; then it is rotated by the magnetic torquing coil into alignment perpendicular to the orbital plane and tangent to the earth's surface. This configuration makes it possible for pictures taken from the $2\frac{1}{2}$-inch, 500-scan-line wide-angle vidicon cameras, canted 26.5 degrees on opposite sides of the satellite's rotational plane, to provide adequate width coverage for full global observation. Under normal operation each camera takes 16 pictures per orbit at 128-second intervals, though the interval can be decreased to 64 or 32 seconds. Two tape recorders capable of storing up to 48 pictures each are used when the satellite is out of range of ground stations in Alaska, California, and Virginia. The satellite carries other instrumentation for the purpose of sensing infrared, long-wave earth radiation. The TOS system is shown in Fig. 2–6.

The Programming Unit of the Weather Bureau's National Weather Satellite Center decides what area is to be photographed during each orbit. The decision is dependent on what areas can be seen by the satellite on each orbit as well as what areas are of most interest to the meteorologists. When the decision has been made, the NASA's Goddard Space Flight Center computes the command to be relayed to the satellite by the data acquisition station. The satellite can be commanded to take pictures with either or both cameras, to store the pictures, and to transmit the pictures to the ground. When the pictures are transmitted to the ground station, they are received on a kinescope (television-type tube) and photographed. The developed film positives are projected onto a geographic grid, so that the weather expert can map the clouds. The cloud map or *nephanalysis* is then transmitted in pictorial form by facsimile and in coded form by teletypewriter to the Meteorological Satellite unit located at Suitland, Maryland, adjacent to the National Meteorological Center. Here the nephanalysis is checked, is used to confirm or add to the standard analysis, and sent to users both in the United States and abroad.

The Nimbus family of weather-reconnaissance satellites are launched into a polar orbit. The plane of the orbit is planned to include a line connecting the earth and the sun. This means that the time at the point directly below the satellite will always be close to local noon or midnight. Nimbus is earth-stabilized, so that the cameras always point to the earth. One takes a still television picture directly downward. The other two are aimed at an angle to the right and left of the track. In this way the entire daylight side of the earth is photographed once daily at the equator and more frequently at high latitudes. (Nimbus I was launched on August 29, 1964.)

Because the earth and clouds have different temperatures, they radiate heat differently. By this means infrared sensors can sometimes distinguish clouds. Each Nimbus has infrared sensing instruments which make radiation observations of clouds on the dark side of the earth. Thus, a record of cloud cover will be available twice a day in the equatorial region.

Meteorological Rockets

We are now living in the age of missiles, and are constantly being reminded that we know very little about the daily changes which take place in that portion of the atmosphere which lies above 100 millibars, other than through the information which comes from periodic meteorological rocket ascents.

Some of the aspects of this region which need study are (1) the climatology of the whole upper atmosphere, including the variation in

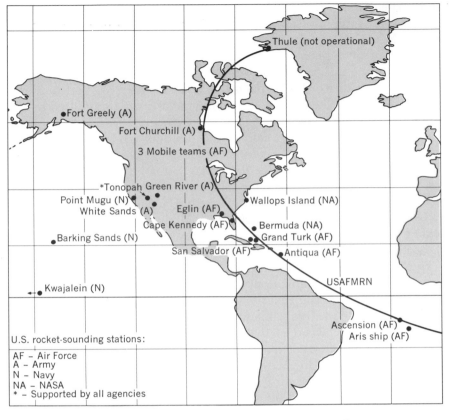

FIG. 2–7
U.S. rocket-sounding stations.

space and time of all the meteorological variables and *particularly* the variation of density and wind, (2) the relation between stratospheric temperature and wind and the distribution of ozone and water vapor, (3) incidence of clouds and aerosols, and (4) the relation between solar activity and the state of the upper atmosphere.

The United States Air Force has taken the lead in the field of meteorological rocketry, having had the vision in the spring of 1962 to propose an operational network of six stations. See Fig. 2–7. Regular network firings were carried on in 1962–1963 until the supply of rockets ran short; but test support firings continue.

Many problems face those who will be developing a synoptic network of meteorological rockets. The Joint Meteorological Rocket Network

Steering Committee (JMRNSC) is charged with the solution of these problems. And this committee moves ahead convinced that meteorological rocketry will have an increased importance in the future.

HOW WET IS THE AIR?

The water-vapor content of the air is one of the most important meteorological variables, and it is one of the most difficult to measure accurately. For this reason we devote additional remarks to a description of the several instruments used and the associated problems.

Hair Hygrometer

There is probably no record of the date when it was first noted that a human hair became longer when the moisture content of the air increased. This led to the development of an instrument called the hair hygrometer for measuring the relative humidity, i.e., the ratio of the actual moisture content of the air to the maximum amount of moisture that can exist in vapor form at a particular air temperature. In such an instrument the changing length of the hair is recorded on a scale (or on a moving drum) through a linkage mechanism, and the scale is calibrated against atmospheres of known humidity. This instrument has been widely used for many years and still suffices for most everyday uses in which high accuracy is not a criterion.

Wet-and-Dry-Bulb Psychrometer

Another type of instrument, called a wet-and-dry-bulb psychrometer, is constructed on thermodynamic principles. It consists of a pair of matched thermometers, the bulb of one of which is covered by a wick saturated with distilled water. When the thermometers are ventilated by whirling or by a fan, the evaporation of the water in the wick cools the surrounding air and the bulb by a certain number of degrees which depends on the moisture content of the air and the temperature. Tables have been prepared from thermodynamic formulas relating dry-bulb temperature, depression of wet-bulb temperature, and relative humidity. The wet-and-dry-bulb psychrometer gives good humidity data except at low temperatures and low humidities. Errors sometimes creep in when the wick becomes dirty or oily. In more recent years psychrometers have been refined through the use of electrical-resistance thermometer bulbs, remote indicators, and recorders.

Electrical-Resistance Hygrometer

For a number of years remote-reading humidity instruments have employed a principle which depends upon the change in electrical resistance of a thin film of a hygroscopic salt, usually lithium chloride. A thin plate of glass or plastic is covered with a film of the salt, and the resistance between the two ends controls the frequency of a radio transmitter. A device of this type is employed in the radiosonde instrument package. A newer type, which yields better humidity data at low temperatures, uses a thin film of a carbon dispersed in a slightly hygroscopic binder. As the humidity increases the binder expands and increases the resistance by slightly separating the carbon particles from each other. Research is currently being carried on with other substances such as an anodic oxide on an aluminum film, plastic polymers, and so on.

Dew-Point Hygrometer

Still another important type of humidity instrument is called the dew-point hygrometer. The dew point is defined as the temperature at which the moisture in the air starts to condense out on an available surface (if the temperature is below freezing, the frost point is the temperature at which frost forms on a surface). In an instrument employing this principle the surface reflectivity of a small mirror is monitored by a photocell. A metallic rod extending from the back of the mirror is cooled by contact with dry ice or liquid freon. The temperature at which dew (or frost) starts to form on the mirror, thus changing the mirror reflectivity, is recorded by a thermocouple in the mirror. The photocell controls a heater element in the mirror so that the mirror temperature remains at the dew point. This instrument (with refinements) is very useful at low temperatures and is widely used in high-altitude stratospheric research.

Still other instruments involving sophistication beyond the scope of this book are *coulemetric, spectroscopic,* and *radio-frequency hygrometers.*

Why is the accurate measurement of humidity important? Aside from the obvious needs in such areas as fog forecasting, it is a critically important variable in the forecasting of cloudiness (a special example of which is aircraft condensation trails) and precipitation. Beyond this it now appears that the small amounts of water vapor present in the stratosphere may be an important tracer by means of which the origin of stratospheric air may be deduced. In the more distant future it is possible that the manipulation of humidity may be an important consideration in attempts to control the weather.

CHAPTER 3

**About
Climate**

*Man is interested in both weather averages and
weather extremes, thus in climate. Climatology
is the statistical aspect of weather, and it has
variations in both space and time. After pre-
senting a brief history of climatology in the
U.S.A. we move to the climatology of temperature, both at the surface and aloft. The latter
leads to the story of the discovery of the
stratosphere and the naming of the several
atmospheric layers: troposphere, tropopause,
stratosphere, stratopause, mesosphere, thermosphere, and exosphere. We conclude with
the climatology of precipitation and pressure,
illustrated by diagrams.*

It has been said that the one thing which is certain about the weather is its variability. When we use the term "the weather," we refer to the full gamut of meteorological variables discussed in the previous chapter (temperature, pressure, etc.). Man is much concerned about the weather because of his involvement with and in it. Not only is he interested in the "usual" weather, which represents average values of the weather elements; he is also interested in the "unusual" weather, which represents departures from these average values. One of the principal reasons for taking weather observations is to establish the *climatology* of different localities.

ASPECTS OF CLIMATOLOGY

A vast number of observations have been collected over a period of years. The following table shows the stations with the longest uninterrupted series of observations.

Year of start	Station	Country
1664	Paris	France
1692	Breslau	Germany (now Poland)
1700	Berlin	Germany
1722	Upsala	Sweden
1723	Lund	Sweden
1725	Padua	Italy
1725	Leningrad	Russia
1779	New Haven	United States

Of course there are many thousands of additional stations, some of which have been gathering weather data for a century or more. Clearly, one of the major tools of climatology must be statistics, that branch of mathematics which deals with means of reducing large populations of numerical data to manageable and meaningful form. Modern technology is exploited to the full in solving the physical problem of handling the vast quantities of data.

The National Weather Records Center is the depository of climatological information. Weather records are routinely entered on punched cards for expeditious handling by data-processing machines. The punched-card library at the Center now contains about 500,000,000 cards and is growing by about 40,000,000 per year. Since the cards tend to be bulky and deteriorate with age, they are microfilmed for permanent storage. Photographs of 13,000 cards are placed on a 100-foot roll of 16-millimeter film. A high-speed electronic film reader has been built and put in operation, thus making microfilm practical as a machine data-processing medium. This reader searches the columns of the card images for plugboard-specified categories of data. The newest version of the reader will possess the option of either punching cards at 250 per minute, writing the data on magnetic tape at 2000 full-card images per minute, or direct input of the data to an electronic computer. One can foresee the eventual development of the automatic weather station, which will produce a punched paper-tape record directly from the observing instruments. This record will then be funneled directly into the Records Center without the touch of a human hand.

Climatology has a space variable: the *area* of climatological concern. It also has a time variable: the *period* over which the data are gathered, and the *period* over which the variation is to be computed. It is known from statistics that the larger the sample of data, the more representative will be the average computed from it. Thus the average maximum temperature during the month of July in Paris would be known much more reliably than the same average computed for a station established in 1950. Furthermore, no two areas should be compared climatologically unless the periods of observation from both make a reasonable match.

Evidently, there are many ways in which the accumulated data can be handled statistically. The most frequent are the common average, or mean value, and the maximum and minimum departures from the mean, i.e., the extremes. The raw information may be organized along geographical lines in such a way as to give physical facts underlying climatic conditions. This is generally referred to as *descriptive climatology*. This branch of climatology is of particular interest to geographers, and to various groups in society who have some need for this type of weather information. In a second branch of climatology, termed *physical climatology*, the major concern is to analyze the accumulated data and sort out the counterplay of cause and effect. The former branch is concerned with the question "what," the latter with "why."

Climate is not a static concept. Climates change with time, but with respect to man's lifetime the change is very slow. Over a long span of time there may be dramatic changes.

The science of past climates is known as paleoclimatology. The evidence available is primarily geological: fossil remains, prints in sediments of organisms, animals and plants. Meteorological information is inferred from this. For instance, presence of vegetation suggests absence of glaciation, abundance of reptiles is related to the mildness of winters, and so on. A second kind of evidence has to do with the inorganic sediments which indicate whether erosion was due to wind, water, or ice.

The evidence indicates that, in times past, tropical or subtropical vegetation covered the temperate zones of North America and Europe.

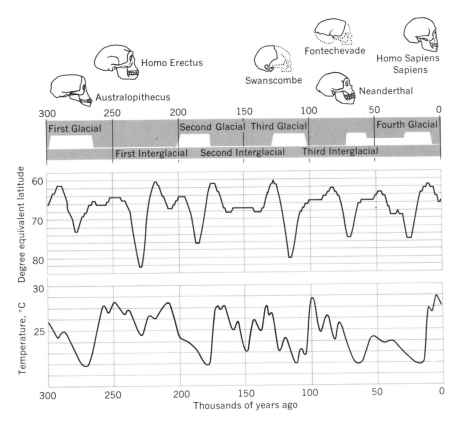

FIG. 3–1
Temperature fluctuations during the four glacial periods. After C. Emiliana,
"Ancient Temperatures," *Scientific American*, February 1958, p. 61, by permission.

Greenland and Antarctica were not covered by ice. Coral reefs reached
as far north as Spitzbergen. Periodically, for relatively short time spans,
sheets of ice did build up and moved well into the middle latitudes.
Why they did is a riddle to which there is no satisfactory answer as yet.
The time scale involved and variation in mean temperatures are shown
schematically in Fig. 3–1.

HISTORY

When did the idea of climatology arise in the U.S.A.? Most of the American weather records from the 1700's were kept by individuals to satisfy
their curiosity. Apparently the idea of a systematic survey of meteorological conditions did not emerge until the end of this century.

We find that the official beginning of climatological observations stemmed from an order issued by Dr. J. Tilton, the Surgeon General of the Army, on May 2, 1814, as a collateral duty of the hospital surgeon: "He shall keep a diary of the weather." By 1818 data from a score of army posts were coming into the office. Here they were compiled and summarized. These were published in 1826 by Dr. J. Lovell, then Surgeon General. His successor, Dr. T. Lawson, brought out another volume of summarized data in 1840. And another young surgeon, Dr. S. Forry, produced the first scientific climatology of the United States in 1842: *The Climate of the United States and Its Endemic Influences* (New York: J. and H. G. Langley, 378 pp.).

The history of climatology then moves into the period of J. Henry, brilliant physicist and administrator of the Smithsonian Institution, Washington, D.C. One of the major meteorological undertakings of the day was to arrive at an understanding of the nature of traveling storms, and to accomplish this more observation stations were necessary. Henry expanded the existing network of stations and secured the services of two unusual men, Dr. A. H. Guyot and L. Blodget. Guyot wrote instructions, calibrated and installed instruments, and constructed the famous *Smithsonian Meteorological Tables*. Blodget had great aptitude for statistical work, and was given the task of bringing together and evaluating all past meteorological records in the United States. This work emerged in 1857 as a full-length (536-page) book: *Climatology of the United States and of the Temperate Latitudes of the North American Continent* (Philadelphia: J. B. Lippincott & Co.). This book remains very readable even today.

In 1870 the activities of the Smithsonian Institution were taken over by a national weather service, at first under the direction of the Army Signal Corps. Responsibility for climatology was given to Lt. H. H. C. Dunwoody, who later became Assistant Chief of the Weather Bureau in 1890 after its establishment in the Department of Agriculture.

In the following section we consider the climatology of the principal weather elements.

CLIMATOLOGY OF TEMPERATURE

Surface

The mean temperature and the range of temperature are the most important climatological elements. There is such a close link between temperature and biological activity that "How hot (or cold) is it?" is usually the first climatological question asked by man.

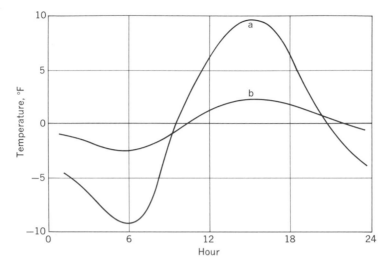

FIG. 3–2
Diurnal variation of air temperature on (a) clear and (b) cloudy days. Data gathered at Washington, D.C., in September–October. Each curve is a mean of 10 days. From H. E. Landsberg, *Physical Climatology*, 2nd ed., Du Bois, Pa.: Gray Printing Co., Inc., 1958, by permission.

The temperature at any station shows a cyclic variation. This may be over a 24-hour period, a period of a year, or a period of eons. We are familiar with the first two periods. We must refer to paleoclimatology for information on the third.

The 24-hour cycle is caused by the rotation of the earth on its axis. The size of the variation, or the deviation from the average, depends on several factors. The most striking is the presence or absence of cloudiness. (See Fig. 3–2.)

The 365-day cycle is caused by the tilt of the earth's axis by an angle of 23.5 degrees from the plane of its orbit around the sun. The vernal (March 21) and autumnal (September 23) equinoxes occur when the noon sun is overhead at the equator. On June 21 (the summer solstice) the noon sun is overhead at 23.5° N latitude; on December 21 (the winter solstice) the noon sun is overhead at 23.5° S latitude. The seasons, of course, are dictated by this apparent march of the sun north and south during the 365-day period. The effect is shown in the charts of isotherms (lines of equal temperature) of mean temperature over the United States in January and July; see Figs. 3–3 and 3–4.[*] These show that the greatest seasonal change in temperature in the United States is about 30°C and

* These two figures also are from H. E. Landsberg, *Physical Climatology*, Gray Printing Co., by permission.

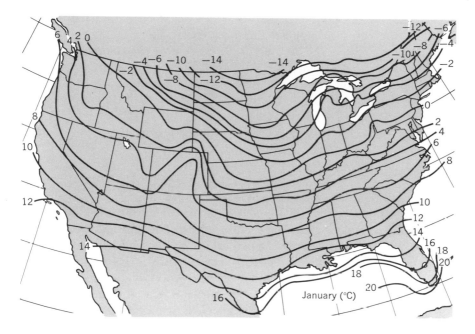

FIG. 3-3. Mean January isotherms, °C, U.S.A.

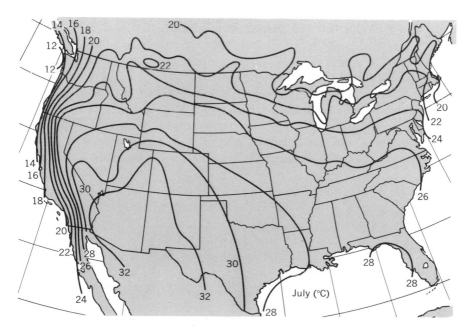

FIG. 3-4. Mean July isotherms, °C, U.S.A.

takes place in the far Northeast. Further evidence of the moderating effect of the ocean is seen on the west coast. Here the isotherms are very close together both in summer and winter. In summer this is a consequence of hot air covering the Pacific Southwest region adjacent to the relatively "cool" ocean. In winter it is a consequence of cold air invading the western United States adjacent to the relatively "warm" ocean. The reasons why the ocean exhibits this moderating effect will emerge when we discuss the physical properties of water.

Upper Air

We now turn our attention to the vertical distribution of temperature.

A great number of vertical penetrations of the atmosphere have been made by kites, balloons, airplanes, and rockets. The information gathered by the weather instruments carried aloft by these devices has been analyzed. As a result we now possess a reasonably complete understanding of the structure of the atmosphere, which will now be presented.

We start by observing that the atmosphere is heated from below, first, by being in contact with the earth which is warmed by absorption of solar energy, and second, through the absorption by water vapor and carbon dioxide of the radiation given off by the earth. (There are two important exceptions to this generalization, as we shall see.) This being the case, we would expect to find a general cooling in the atmosphere with respect to height. The precise rate is called the *lapse rate*. When the lapse rate is large or, as we say, *unstable,* there is a large amount of turbulence, vertical mixing, and overturning. When the lapse rate is so great that the air density increases with elevation, the overturning is violent and spawns the tornado. (As we shall see in a later chapter, the tornado is a very complex mechanism and still not well understood.) This is a limiting situation which is not often encountered. When the lapse rate is zero, the atmosphere is said to be in an *isothermal* (constant temperature) state. Sometimes the lapse rate has a negative value; i.e., the temperature increases with elevation. A layer in which this temperature distribution is found is called an *inversion* and has a very *stable* lapse rate. In such a layer vertical motions are inhibited. These several lapse rates are shown in Fig. 3–5.

Here we digress to sketch out the story of the development of the names *troposphere* and *stratosphere,* and put the discovery of the first exception (mentioned above) in its historical perspective. In the late 19th century there was little knowledge of the temperature distribution in the upper air. The evidence at this time seemed to indicate a steady decrease of air temperature toward the absolute zero of outer space. The

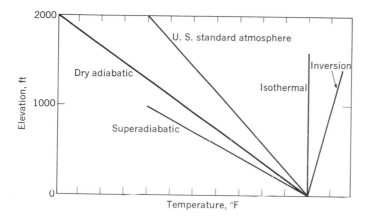

FIG. 3–5.   Examples of various lapse rates.

lower temperatures atop the highest mountains confirmed this idea. It also seemed reasonable that a temperature decrease should accompany the lowering of pressure at the outer reaches of the atmosphere.

The excellent scientific work of a French meteorologist, Léon Phillipe Teisserence de Bort, who established a private observatory near Versailles in 1896, showed that the atmosphere had some surprises up its sleeve. In 1898 De Bort began his series of *ballons-sondes* (balloons carrying meteorographs). A significant record came from a flight made on June 8, 1898. The temperature record showed the normal decrease to a height of 11.8 kilometers (38,700 feet). Then the temperature *remained constant* to 13 kilometers (42,640 feet), the top of the ascent. So ingrained was the assumption that the free-air temperature should always decrease that these data were written off to error.

By 1902 De Bort had records from 236 balloon ascents, 74 of which attained 14 kilometers (45,920 feet) in height. These covered all seasons, night and day. His report to the French Academy was made in April, 1902:

> These observations allow us to study for the first time the temperature in the zone above 10 km putting into light new and unexpected facts of which the most salient now follow.

> 1. Whereas in the mean, the lapse of temperature with height increases and attains in the regions already explored a value rather close to that which corresponds to the adiabatic changes of dry air, this decrease, instead of maintaining itself successively with height, as one had supposed, passes through a maximum, then diminishes rapidly, in order to become nearly zero at an altitude which is, in the mean, in our regions, 11 km.

2. Starting from a height that varies with the atmospheric situation (8 km to 12 km) a zone commences characterized by a very weak decrease of temperature or even a slight increase. We are not able to specify the thickness of this zone, but, from actual observations, it appears to extend for several kilometers.

In 1908, at a meeting of the German Meteorological Society, De Bort suggested a name for the atmospheric layer he had discovered, in a paper titled "The Division of the Atmosphere into Troposphere and Stratosphere from Results of the Exploration of the High Atmosphere."

The term "troposphere" (Gr. *tropos,* "turn") for the lower layer is descriptive of this layer's convective and mixing characteristics; the term "stratosphere" (Lat. *stratum,* "layer") for the upper layer is descriptive of its stability, its lack of convection and mixing. This nomenclature is still in use.

We now know that the average depth of the *troposphere* is about 40,000 feet (8 miles), and that it contains more than 80 percent of the mass of the atmosphere. The upper limit of the troposphere, called the *tropopause,* is higher in the tropics (about 55,000 feet) and lower in the polar regions (as low as 25,000 feet). At the tropopause the temperature falls to as low as $-80°C$ ($-112°F$) over the tropics. In the polar regions the temperature of the tropopause is, on the average, $-55°C$ ($-67°F$).

As De Bort discovered, the troposphere is topped by a layer of air, which he called the *stratosphere,* in which the temperature remains constant or increases. Because of its temperature distribution this layer is stratified (hence the name) and there is little vertical mixing. The stratosphere extends to an altitude of about 30 miles, i.e., to the stratopause.

The *stratopause* is a layer of maximum temperature, which, surprisingly, may be higher than the temperature at the ground. This coincides with the top of a layer of ozone gas (triatomic oxygen), and the high temperature is the result of the ability of this ozone to absorb ultraviolet solar energy. (This is the first of the two exceptions mentioned earlier, p. 58.)

Above the stratopause the temperature again decreases to a height of about 50 miles. This layer is called the *mesosphere* (Gr. *meso,* "middle"). The top of the mesosphere is called the *mesopause,* and here we find the lowest temperature in the atmosphere, about $-140°C$ ($-220°F$).

Above the mesopause the temperature rises rapidly with height in the region of the atmosphere called the *thermosphere.* The high temperature in this region is caused by the presence of atomic oxygen which absorbs

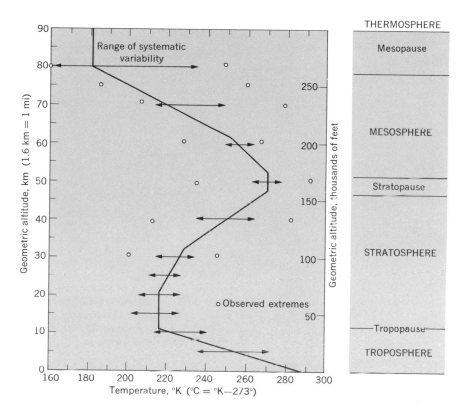

FIG. 3–6

U.S. standard atmosphere (1962) and range of systematic variability. To convert temperatures from °K to °C subtract 273.

energy from a selected portion of the solar beam. The thermosphere includes that region of the atmosphere which contains a relatively high concentration of charged particles (electrons and ions), and is sometimes referred to as the *ionosphere*. This is a significant region to communications scientists, for these electrically charged layers can reflect radio waves back to earth.

At about 350 miles the atmosphere becomes very thin. The "air" consists of isolated molecules and atoms which move long distances between collisions. This is the beginning of the *exosphere*, the outer fringe of the atmosphere, where one encounters the Van Allen radiation belts, and through which the earth satellites (such as Tiros) pursue their orbital paths. For a diagrammatic representation of these several layers, see Fig. 3–6.

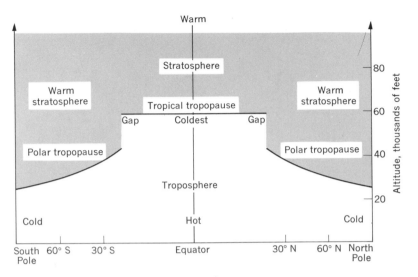

FIG. 3–7
Pole-to-pole vertical cross section showing
variation in height of tropopause. After
J. Spar, *Earth, Sea, and Air: A Survey of the
Geological Sciences*, Reading, Massachusetts:
Addison-Wesley, 1962.

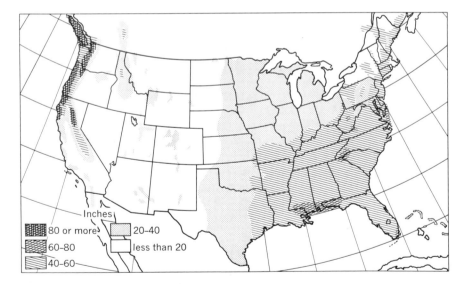

FIG. 3–8
Mean annual rainfall in the United States.
After Landsberg, *Physical Climatology*, Gray
Printing Co., by permission.

Figure 3–7 summarizes the changes one encounters in the atmospheric layers along a pole-to-pole vertical cross section of the atmosphere. We note the high, cold tropical tropopause and the low, warm polar tropopause. These two tropopauses overlap in the subtropics, where, of necessity, there is a gap or break in the tropopause.

In the troposphere, the temperature falls from the equator toward the poles. In the lower stratosphere the temperature is lowest over the equator and increases toward the poles. These facts of the atmospheric temperature distribution have significant consequences which will be developed in Chapter 5.

CLIMATOLOGY OF PRECIPITATION

A second weather variable which is of prime importance to man is precipitation. Man must have water to live. If it does not fall from the skies in ample quantities, he must transport it to the place of need or he must distill it. Climatologist R. DeC. Ward has proposed convenient climatic intervals in his book.

Climate	Annual precipitation
True desert	Less than 5 in.
Arid	5–10 in.
Semi-arid	10–20 in.
Moderately humid	20–40 in.
Humid	40–80 in.
Excessive rainfall	More than 80 in.

The chart of mean annual rainfall in the United States (shown in Fig. 3–8) is plotted according to these intervals. Here it is seen that excessive precipitation falls in the coastal and inland mountains (the Cascades) of the far west and northwest regions. Yet most of the western portion of the United States has an arid climate. Why the distribution of precipitation should be as it is will become clearer in subsequent chapters.

CLIMATOLOGY OF PRESSURE

The seasonal variation in the distribution of pressure over the northern hemisphere is seen by comparing Figs. 3–9 and 3–10, which give normal sea-level pressures for January and July. In January high pressure dominates the continents and low pressure dominates the northern oceans. In July the oceans are dominated by high pressure, the continents by low pressure.

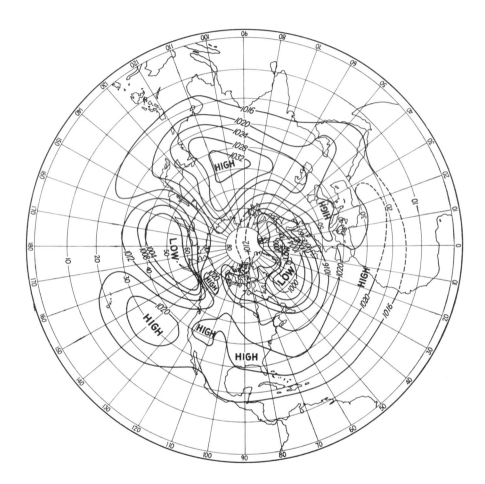

FIG. 3–9
January mean sea-level pressures, mb, plotted on a
Northern-Hemisphere polar map. From H. R. Byers,
General Meteorology, 3rd ed., New York: McGraw-Hill,
1959, by permission.

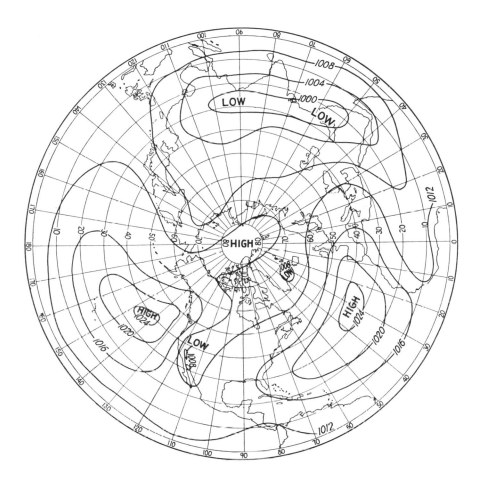

FIG. 3–10
July mean sea-level pressures, mb, plotted on a Northern-
Hemisphere polar map. From Byers, *General Meteorology*,
McGraw-Hill, by permission.

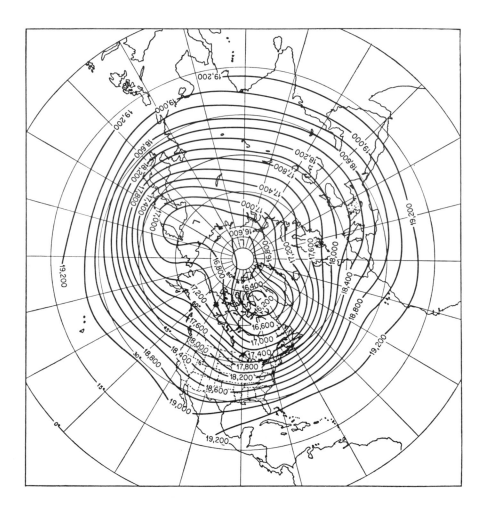

FIG. 3–11
January normal contours of 500-mb surface plotted on a
Northern-Hemisphere polar map. From Byers, *General
Meteorology*, McGraw-Hill, by permission.

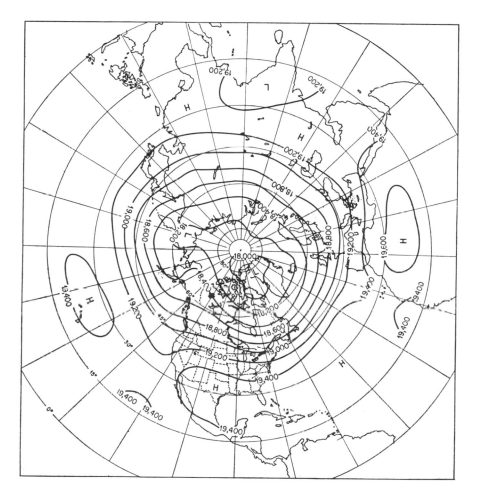

FIG. 3–12
July normal contours of 500-mb surface plotted on a
Northern-Hemisphere polar map. From Byers, *General
Meteorology*, McGraw-Hill, by permission.

Figures 3–11 and 3–12 show the upper-air pressure distribution by plotting the height of a given (500-millibar) pressure surface. In January this surface dips down sharply in a bowl shape to low values over the poles. In July the slope of the contour is much more shallow. We will examine the physical causes and consequences of these patterns in our discussion of the general circulation. At this point we are interested only in stating what the mean conditions happen to be.

CHAPTER 4

**Radiation:
Incoming
and
Outgoing**

We open this chapter by introducing and defining basic terms which will be used frequently throughout the remainder of the book: energy, work, kinetic and potential energy, radiation, convection, and conduction. The fourth-power radiation law, the wave equation, and the electromagnetic spectrum of radiant energy are described. This leads to special consideration of radiation of wavelength between 0.4 and 0.7 micron, which is light. Next is an explanation of the solar constant. We follow the solar beam as it enters the atmosphere and is depleted by reflection, absorption, and scattering. Albedo is defined. Then we turn our attention to outgoing long-wave (1–100 microns) infrared radiation. We see that, because incoming solar radiation exceeds outgoing terrestrial radiation in the equatorial regions, there must be atmospheric convection on a giant scale to transport the excess heat energy poleward.

DEFINITION OF TERMS

Before commencing our study of the energy balance in the atmosphere we need to introduce some basic ideas with which the reader may not be familiar. What is *energy?* The term is used in many ways. The physicist says it is what enables *work* to be done. In a less precise sense, this is what the housewife means when she says that she gets up feeling "full of energy." On this day the housework gets done. The concept *work,* to the physicist, involves the application of a *force* to move an object, which may be a mountain or a molecule, through a given distance in the direction of the force. When work is done, the object may be given energy of motion, which we call *kinetic energy,* or it may be given energy of position in a gravitational field, which we call *potential energy,* or it may be *warmed* by the effects of friction. Both work and energy are expressed in foot-pounds in the English system of units, or in joules in the metric (mks, meter-kilogram-second) system.

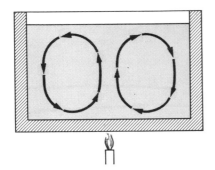

FIG. 4-1
Heat transferred through a container entirely by conduction, and throughout the liquid by convection cell. Conduction plays a lesser role in the liquid.

It also works the other way around. Heat energy may be expended to do work. The automobile is a good example of this. Gasoline possesses chemical potential energy. When gas in vapor form is mixed with air and burned, this energy is changed to heat energy. The thermal energy is then expended to do work in overcoming inertia and friction, thus accelerating the mass of the automobile and riders, and producing heat.

Our problem is not unlike this in broad outline. The atmosphere of the earth can be thought of as a giant thermodynamic machine which takes in its fuel from the sun and converts it to heat energy, some of which is used up in overcoming the inertia of the air, some in overcoming the frictional drag of the atmosphere over the surface of the earth. The remainder is sent back to space.

The question of how energy is transported from one place to another is an essential part of the problem. We find that there are three distinctly different methods. The first is electromagnetic *radiation*. The physicist has found that all space is pervaded by interrelated electric and magnetic fields. Energy "rides" on waves set up in these fields, which move through vacuous space at a speed of 186,000 miles/second, the speed of light. The second is *convection*. In this case the heated medium is physically transported from one position in space to another. The third is molecular *conduction*. In this case heat energy is transferred by molecular impact, the more active (hotter) molecules setting their near neighbors into more violent agitation by colliding with them. A simple example of conduction and convection is provided in Fig. 4–1. Having established these basic definitions we are now prepared to see their application in nature.

INCOMING RADIATION

Description of Radiation

Our sun is an average star as stars go. It is neither very old nor very young, very large nor very small, very hot nor very cold, very dense nor very tenuous. Its diameter is 865,000 miles, or 100 times that of the earth. Its surface temperature is about 5800 degrees on the Kelvin scale (in which 0°C corresponds to 273°K). Deep in the interior of the sun the temperature rises to hundreds of millions of degrees. Most of the atoms comprising the sun are hydrogen. In the interior depths, where the density is 100 times that of lead and the temperatures are so high, hydrogen is continuously being fused into helium. The excess mass of the four hydrogen nuclei over that of one resultant helium nucleus is converted to energy in strict accordance with Einstein's equation, $E = mc^2$ (where E is the energy, m is the mass, and c is the speed of light). This energy rises to the surface by convection and radiation, and replaces that lost by radiation from the surface. For each new helium nucleus formed, 4.5×10^{-12} joule of radiant energy is released. Since the luminosity of the sun is 3.8×10^{26} joules/second, about 10^{38} new helium nuclei are being produced in the sun each second.

It is a fundamental fact of nature that all bodies radiate energy from their surfaces. Some are efficient radiators, and others are inefficient ones, depending on the characteristics of their surfaces. Radiators which are 100 percent efficient are called *blackbodies*. Likewise, all bodies absorb energy which falls on their surfaces, some efficiently and others inefficiently. Again the efficiency depends on the nature of the surface. A

19th-century physicist, Stefan, determined that the maximum energy output of a radiating body was proportional to the fourth power of the radiating temperature (expressed in Kelvin degrees); thus,

$$E \propto T^4.$$

This relation means that if the Kelvin temperature of a radiating body were doubled, its energy output would be increased by 2^4 or $2 \times 2 \times 2 \times 2 = 16$ times. If the temperature were quadrupled, the energy output would be increased by 4^4, or $4 \times 4 \times 4 \times 4 = 256$ times, and so on.

The German physicist Wien discovered a further fundamental fact having to do with radiation: the wavelength at which the maximum radiation is emitted varies inversely with the temperature, decreasing as the temperature rises. This explains why hotter stars tend toward blue and cooler stars tend toward red. It also explains why the radiation from the earth must be detected by instruments sensitive to infrared radiation, and why radiation from some very cool stars can be detected only by collecting their radiation with the antenna of a radio telescope.

We have mentioned the wave motion in the electromagnetic field. We now must clarify the concept of "wavelength." Wave motion is described in terms of the *length* of the wave, the *speed* of the wave, and the *frequency* of the oscillation. These three factors are related to one another in a simple but very important equation known as the wave equation, expressed as

$$c = f\lambda,$$

where c is the speed of the wave, f is its frequency, and λ (lambda) is the wavelength.

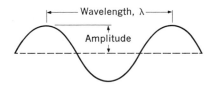

FIG. 4-2
Schematic of wave illustrating wavelength, λ, the distance from crest to crest.

If we think for the moment in terms of water waves because of their familiarity, we could represent a wave as shown in Fig. 4-2. One *wavelength* is defined as the distance between successive crests (or troughs); the frequency is the number of crests which would pass a given check point in a specific interval of time (such as a second). As we have seen, the product of the wavelength and frequency gives the speed of the wave.

Water waves have wavelengths ranging from a few tenths of an inch, for ripple waves, to a few hundreds of miles for the earthquake-generated *tsunami* (tidal wave). The average wavelength of water waves is a few feet.

In the case of electromagnetic waves there is an even larger range of wavelengths, as shown in Fig. 4–3, which portrays the so-called electromagnetic spectrum. The unit of wavelength used to describe waves in the central region of the electromagnetic spectrum is the micron (sometimes represented by the Greek letter mu, μ). The micron is one-millionth of a meter, one ten-thousandth of a centimeter, or one-thousandth of a millimeter.

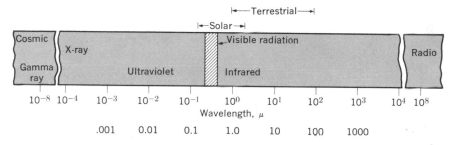

FIG. 4–3
Electromagnetic spectrum emphasizing central region. Hatched portion is visible spectrum (0.4–0.72 micron). The sun radiates most intensely in this region. The earth radiates at longer, invisible infrared wavelengths.

What range of wavelengths brackets the output of energy of a radiating body whose surface temperature is about 6000°K? Analysis of the data from which Fig. 4–4 was drawn shows that 99 percent of the sun's radiation falls between 0.15 and 4.0 microns.

Furthermore, because of a strange set of circumstances, human beings have a network of nerve endings, terminating in a small spot behind their eyeballs, which respond to the stimulus provided by electromagnetic waves whose wavelengths range between 0.4 and 0.74 micron. This enables us *to see* a certain set of phenomena. For instance, since 45 percent of the sun's radiation happens to lie rather evenly distributed in this wavelength region, it yields the sensation of white. Since the sky radiation is strongest in the short-wavelength region, the mind receives the sensation "blue." When the sun shines through the atmosphere at dawn or dusk the longer-wavelength radiation is less depleted than the short and the sun appears red. This effect is accentuated when the air is dusty or smoky.

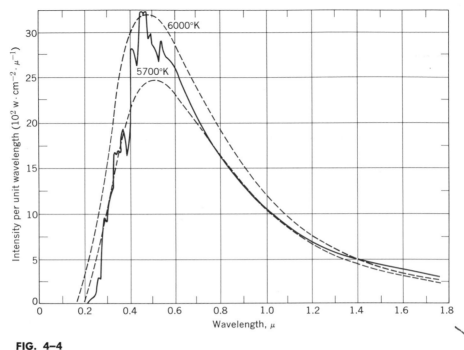

FIG. 4–4
Solar spectrum (solid line) and blackbody (i.e., 100% efficient) radiation
at 5700°K and 6000°K. After D. Johnson, *Journal of Meteorology*
11 (1954), 431.

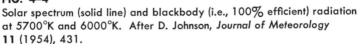

Another 45 percent of the sun's radiation can be felt but not seen. Its
wavelength exceeds 0.74 micron and is designated as *infrared*. Nine percent of the sun's radiation consists of wavelengths shorter than 0.4
micron. Figure 4–4 shows a graph of the energy emission, by wavelengths, of the sun and ideal radiators at 6000°K and 5700°K.

Depletion of the Solar Beam

We now have enough background in radiation physics to focus our
attention on the earth and see what happens to the tiny fraction of the
sun's radiation which it intercepts. Viewed from several thousand miles'
distance, the earth appears as a bluish-tinged spheroid. This color results
from the presence of a transparent gaseous layer which scatters the blue
component in the sun's rays more effectively than the red. Masses of
opaque cloud ranging up to thousands of miles in horizontal extent float
in the lower layers of this atmosphere, undergoing complex patterns
of development and dissipation.

At earth-distance nearly 2.0 calories of energy passes through each square centimeter perpendicular to the sun's beam each minute, as seen in Fig. 4–5. This value is alternatively expressed as nearly 2.0 langleys per minute. This is a power income of one-half million horsepower per square mile. Since the largest cross-section area of the earth is about fifty million square miles, where the radius of the earth is 4000 miles, we can calculate the rate of receipt of solar energy at the outer boundary of the atmosphere to be 210 million million horsepower!

Now we must deal with the complications, and they are legion. In the first place, Fig. 4–5 shows from geometrical considerations that a square mile of surface area located at high latitudes would receive less solar energy than the same area located at the equator. From this fact alone we would expect the tropics to be warmer than the polar regions.

The solar beam must pass through the atmosphere on its way to the earth, and is partially depleted in the course of doing so. High in the exosphere, molecules of oxygen (O_2) absorb some of the photons of radiation, and the added energy is sufficient to cause the molecules to break apart, leaving atomic oxygen (O). The minimum energy required for this reaction corresponds to a wavelength of 0.2424 micron. Reactions involving atomic and molecular oxygen and a third body then form ozone (O_3). Ozone gas becomes most concentrated at altitudes ranging from 15 to 20 miles. It performs a significant function by acting as an opaque window, absorbing all solar radiation shorter than 0.3 micron in wavelength. In this way the lethal short-wavelength ultraviolet radiation is kept from the surface of the earth.

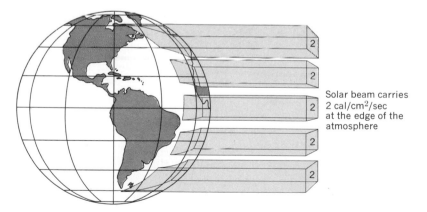

Solar beam carries
2 cal/cm²/sec
at the edge of the
atmosphere

FIG. 4–5
Schematic of inflow of solar energy at earth-distance at time of equinox. The beam is depleted as it enters the earth's atmosphere and is spread over a greater surface area at high latitudes.

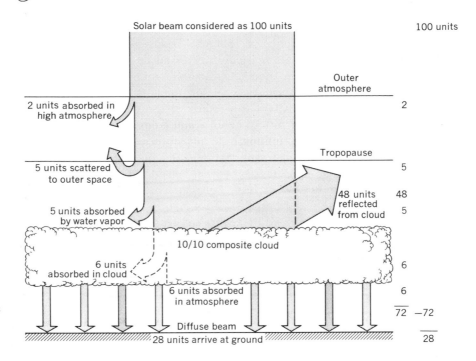

FIG. 4–6
Depletion of solar beam as it penetrates
the atmosphere on an overcast day.

The absorption of this extreme short-wavelength radiation by the ozone layer, representing but a small fraction of the total energy in the beam, gives rise to a region at great heights in which the temperature, surprisingly, is about as warm as it is at sea level during the summer. (See Fig. 3–7.)

As the solar beam penetrates the atmosphere it is substantially depleted by reflection from the upper surface of the cloud layers present; minor portions are scattered by the intervening molecules and dust particles. (It is because the air molecules scatter the short wavelengths of the solar beam more intensely than the long that the sky takes on its beautiful blue cast.) Finally the beam reaches the surface of the earth, where part of it is further reflected and the remainder is absorbed.

It is clear that the amount of reflection from cloud layers will depend on their kind and extent. An overcast sky of altostratus would reflect three-quarters of the incident beam back to space. Also, the effectiveness of the earth's surface as a reflector will depend on the inclination of the beam as it falls on the surface and on the nature of the surface itself, whether land or water, snow or ice. In the snow-covered Arctic, where the latitude factor would cause the solar beam to strike the surface at a glancing angle, there would be a high percentage of reflection and very little absorption. The very high temperatures recorded, say, in Death Valley of the southwestern United States, result from the direct onslaught of the solar beam with a minimum of reflection. Obviously this is a complex and highly variable situation. A concept called the *albedo* is commonly used. This is a ratio (the fraction) of the intensity of the reflected to the incoming solar beam. A small albedo means poor reflection and good absorption. A large albedo means good reflection and poor absorption. Albedo is a quantity which can be measured well by weather satellites. So far as the earth is concerned, a good average value of the albedo seems to be about 0.4. That means that on the average 0.6 of the solar beam is absorbed and 0.4 is reflected. We must reckon with this imbalance.

The most involved case of depletion of the solar beam takes place when skies are cloudy. Figure 4–6 shows values worked out for a composite single cloud deck of 10/10 coverage. It is convenient to talk about the intensity of the solar beam which arrives at the outer atmosphere in terms of 100 arbitrary units. In the high atmosphere above the troposphere, 2 units are absorbed. In the high troposphere, 5 units are scattered back to outer space and 5 units are absorbed by water vapor. If we use the figure 0.55 for the albedo of the cloud layer, $0.55 \times 88 = 48$ units would be reflected upward from the cloud. In the interior of the cloud, about 7 percent of the beam is absorbed by the liquid water and water vapor, yielding $0.07 \times 88 = 6$ units. No longer is there a direct solar beam. The cloud transmits a diffuse beam equal to 34 units, 6 additional units of which are absorbed by the atmosphere under the cloud, leaving 28 units to arrive at the ground.

EARTH RADIATION

We now turn our attention to the earth as the radiating body. It is important to remember that, on the average (if we ignore the arctic regions for purposes of simplicity), a certain area experiences the incoming solar beam for only half of the day, and only once from a vertical angle. However, *all* the surface of the earth is radiating energy 24 hours a day. The wavelength for the peak earth radiation is computed at about 10 microns.

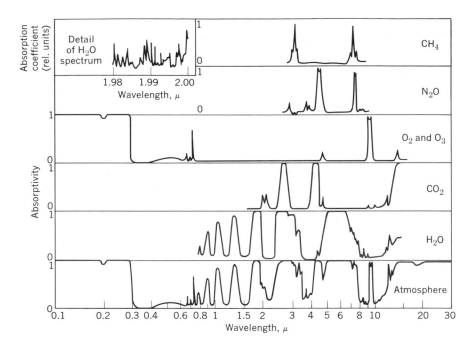

FIG. 4–7

Absorption characteristics of the important atmospheric gases. From R. G. Fleagle and J. A. Businger, *Introduction to Atmospheric Physics*, New York: Academic Press, 1963, p. 153, by permission.

The principal infrared-absorbing gases in the atmosphere are water vapor, carbon dioxide, and ozone, in order of decreasing importance. Each absorbs selectively, i.e., at certain wavelengths, as shown in Fig. 4–7. It should be noted that at the earth's peak radiating wavelength of 10 microns, all three gases present an "open window" to the terrestrial radiation. Aside from this "large opening" the radiation must escape through the remaining "cracks." Radiation of other wavelengths which is absorbed warms the invisible gases which are part of the atmosphere. The absorption of a fraction of the solar beam by the earth, and the absorption of the earth's long-wave radiation, are sometimes referred to as the *greenhouse effect*. A more precise term would be the *atmosphere effect*.

The detailed analysis of the outward flow of terrestrial radiation is vastly more complex than that of the inward flow of solar radiation because of the continually changing distributions of earth and air temperature, water vapor content of the air, and cloudiness. However, in general, the maximum radiation would take place in the subtropics under clear skies, because there the mean temperatures are highest. When the skies are overcast the terrestrial radiation is trapped by the clouds and the effective radiating surface becomes the cold stratosphere; thus, the net radiation is low. In the polar regions the clouds and the earth are at about the same temperature and radiate equally well.

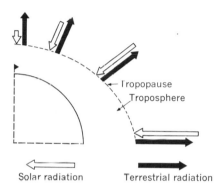

Solar radiation   Terrestrial radiation

FIG. 4–8
Vertical radiative transport of heat.
After G. J. Haltiner and F. L. Martin,
Dynamical and Physical Meteorology,
New York: McGraw-Hill, 1957.

When incoming and outgoing radiations are compared at different latitudes, they are equal only at 38 degrees, as shown in Fig. 4–8. On the low-latitude side, solar radiation exceeds terrestrial radiation; on the high-latitude side, terrestrial exceeds solar radiation. Since the earth shows no tendency to get hotter or colder, we reason that the excess heat in the tropics must be moved physically to higher latitudes. This means convection on a giant scale, which is the equivalent of air circulation over the earth's surface. We now turn to this topic.

CHAPTER 5

**The
Atmosphere
in
Motion**

*To understand atmospheric motion we need to
understand the behavior of a gas in terms of
pressure, density, and temperature. We discuss
the general gas law, $p = \rho RT$, with examples of
increasing complexity. Archimedes' principle
is presented to introduce the concept of buoyancy. Using an oversimplified model of the
earth we show how a Hadley circulation cell
develops. But since the earth rotates, we must
introduce the concept of angular momentum.
Examples of increasing sophistication are developed to show how this principle applies to motion
of the atmosphere. The Coriolis force is discussed. Assuming the prior existence of a
nonuniform distribution of atmospheric pressure,
we develop the concept of the geostrophic wind
and show why the wind blows parallel to
straight isobars under balanced forces. The
topic is then broadened to include flow parallel
to curved isobars. Next we consider how temperature affects air density and hence the height
of a given pressure surface. We discuss contour
maps of upper pressure surfaces and the wave
patterns in the westerly flow aloft. "Trough"
and "ridge" are defined, and the jet stream is
described. The chapter concludes with a
discussion of smaller circulation systems:
monsoonal circulation, land-and-sea breezes,
and mountain-and-valley breezes.*

In this chapter we take the key idea from the last—that the earth experiences a heat surplus in low latitudes and a heat deficit in high latitudes—and spell out the consequences of this "fact of meteorological life" in terms of motion of the atmosphere.

BEHAVIOR OF GASES

General Gas Law

In order to do this properly we must understand some of the characteristic behavior patterns of a gas. We can partially describe a gas in a number of ways: by the *volume* it occupies, by its *temperature* (which is a measure of the kinetic energy of its molecules), by the *pressure* it exerts (which is the net impact force its molecules exert on a unit area), by its *density* (which is the ratio of the mass of the gas contained in a given volume to that volume), and by the number of *moles* of the gas (which is the weight of the gas in grams equal to its molecular weight).

Natural scientists in the late 17th to early 19th centuries intensively investigated the behavior of gases and found that the case for an idealized gas could be summarized in a compact package known as the *general gas law*. This is written as

$$pV = mRT$$

where p is the total pressure of the gas, V is its volume, T is the absolute temperature, m the mass, and R the universal gas constant.

This can be rewritten in a different and more useful form as

$$p = \rho RT,$$

where rho (ρ) is the density.

For convenience this expression can be written in ratio form, where subscripts 1 and 2 refer to two different sets of conditions for the same gas:

$$\frac{p_1}{p_2} = \frac{\rho_1}{\rho_2}\frac{T_1}{T_2}.$$

From this we see that the three variables—the total pressure (i.e., atmospheric pressure plus the reading of the pressure gage), the density, and the Kelvin temperature—are interrelated in a very close-knit fashion. This simple relationship is pregnant with meteorological significance. It is also pregnant with opportunities for confusion when it is applied by the novice to the case of the atmosphere.

Two examples will illustrate the point. First we oversimplify and consider a gas confined in a container with rigid walls. Since both the volume and the mass of the gas are fixed, the density, which is the ratio of mass to volume, is constant. The gas law can then be simplied to

$$p_2 = p_1 \frac{T_2}{T_1}.$$

From this we see that if the temperature increases 10 percent from T_1 to T_2, the pressure must increase 10 percent from p_1 to p_2.

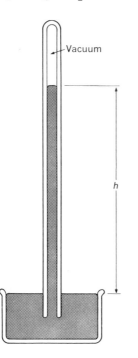

FIG. 5–1

Torricelli's mercury barometer. On the average, the mercury column stands 76.0 cm in height or 29.92 at sea level.

If the gas is contained in an elastic membrane such as a balloon, the situation becomes more complicated. All three variables (p, ρ, and T) are involved. If the balloon is reasonably large, the pressure on the inside and on the outside will be the same. Let us assume that the balloon is filled with a gas which is less dense than air (such as helium) so that the balloon will rise. Further, let us assume that we know both the initial temperature (T_1) and the initial pressure (p_1). The balloon is then released and rises to a level where p_2 and T_2 are known. One can find the new density (ρ_2) by writing

$$\rho_2 = \rho_1 \frac{T_1}{T_2} \frac{p_2}{p_1}.$$

Note that decreases in temperature contribute to an increase in the density, whereas decreases in the pressure contribute to a decrease in the density. The pressure and temperature factors work against each other. The final value of the density is determined by the relative values of the ratios of pressure and temperature. In the atmosphere the pressure term predominates, and as a result the density of the gas in the balloon decreases with increasing altitude.

The case of the atmosphere takes us to an additional stage of complexity. See Fig. 5–1. Each of the other two cases involved gas within a closed container. The atmosphere is enclosed in a "container" which has but one fixed side, namely the surface of the earth. However, because the gas is pulled earthward by the attraction due to gravity, we have a bunching of the air molecules near the earth. In other words, the density of the air decreases with altitude, the pressure of the air decreases with altitude, and as we have seen, the air temperature also decreases though there are exceptions (inversions).

Some numbers may make the situation clearer. If one starts at any given level in the atmosphere, the pressure at 10,000 feet higher is about 70 percent as great as the pressure at the lower level. Or the pressure at 18,500 feet above that level is about 50 percent as great as at the lower level. Or, the pressure 100,000 feet higher is about 1 percent as great as at the lower level.

Thus, at 10,000 feet the pressure would be 700 millibars if the surface pressure were 1000 millibars. At 20,000 feet the pressure would be 0.7×700 or 490 millibars, and so on. Or, putting the matter another way, from sea level to 100,000 feet the pressure would drop by 990 millibars, whereas from 100,000 feet to 200,000 feet the pressure would drop by only 9.9 millibars.

These are rule-of-thumb figures representing average values. When the air is colder than normal, the gas law tells us that the density of the air should increase in comparison to the average density, i.e., that the mass per unit volume should be greater; when the air is warmer the density should be less. This means that the same surface pressure can be exerted by a greater thickness of warm, less dense air, or by a lesser thickness of cold, more dense air. This is a fact of very considerable meteorological significance.

MOTION

Buoyancy

We need to introduce two other fundamental principles of physics before we can apply our information to the subject of atmospheric motion. We go back to the great scientist-engineer Archimedes who clarified the concept of buoyancy. *Archimedes' principle* states that any body immersed in a fluid experiences a buoyant force equal to the weight of the fluid it displaces. Boats float to a level at which they displace a weight of fluid equal to their own weight. A helium-filled balloon displaces a greater weight of air than its own weight because the outside air is more dense than helium. Our experience as children tells us that such a balloon will rise unless restrained from so doing by the string attached to our finger.

Newton's Second Law

Why does the balloon rise? To answer this we need to refer to *Newton's second law of motion*, which states that any object subjected to an unbalanced force will be accelerated, i.e., its speed will be changed with time, in the direction of the unbalanced force, and this acceleration will be inversely proportional to the mass of the body. Thus a buoyant force will exert an upward accelerating force on the body so long as it is not counterbalanced by a downward force of equal value.

We now start to investigate atmospheric motion with a model which involves four simplifying assumptions about the earth:

(1) no rotation,
(2) uniform surface,
(3) equal illumination over the equator from all sides, and
(4) no water vapor in the air.

Such a model is shown schematically in Fig. 5–2.

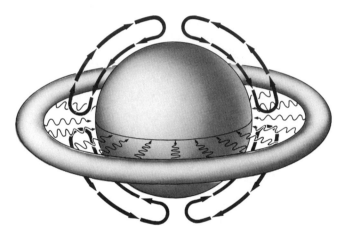

FIG. 5–2
Schematic of a uniform-surface, nonrotating globe receiving radiation from a tubular "sun." The resulting convection is called a Hadley Cell after the discoverer. Scale is distorted.

As a result of the excess of incoming energy at the equator, the warmer, less dense air over the warm surface would be forced to rise because of the buoyant forces exerted upon it. The more dense air over the poles would sink because of the greater gravitational pull and would glide equatorward in the low levels, whereas there would be a compensating poleward drift in the high troposphere. This is the model developed by George Hadley, an 18th-century Englishman. The cellular circulation is known as a *Hadley cell*. The presence of a layer of warm air aloft and cold air at the surface would result in a general downward shift of the center of gravity of the atmosphere. This would result in a change of potential to kinetic energy, or energy of position to energy of motion.

Angular Momentum

As the ideal (say, in political life) is frequently overshadowed by the harsh reality (of vote-getting), here likewise the simple Hadley cellular motion is obscured by the complexities of rotation over a real earth. After all, this *is* a rotating globe; the surface *is* nonuniform both as to substance and contour; it *is* unequally illuminated. In order to understand the effects of the earth's rotation we must introduce still other fundamental principles of physics. All bodies in motion possess a property called momentum. For a body moving in a straight path its linear momentum is the product of its mass and velocity; thus $M = mv$. If it moves in a circular path, its angular momentum is defined by the product of the body's mass, linear velocity, and the radius of curvature of the path. Thus

Newton discerned that the momentum of a body will remain constant unless some external agency steps in, so to speak, and exerts an unbalanced force on the body to change the value of its momentum. This is known as the *principle of conservation of momentum*, and it is a very important generalization of the way nature behaves. This principle is nicely illustrated in the following simple experiment. Tie a stone to a string and thread the string through a piece of tubing. Swing the stone in a circular path of radius R around a vertical axis, holding the tubing fixed. The stone now has a certain angular momentum. As one pulls in on the string, decreasing R, the stone is found to rotate more rapidly (v' increases), as illustrated in Fig. 5–3.

Now we apply this line of reasoning to the case of motion over the earth's surface. Imagine an object, not fixed to the earth, located at rest at the equator (Fig. 5–4). Its linear west-to-east velocity with respect to a fixed position in space would initially be 25,000 miles/24 hours, or a little more than 1000 miles/hour. The radius would be the equatorial

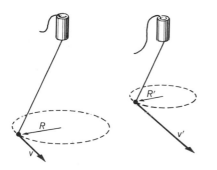

FIG. 5–3
Conservation of angular momentum.

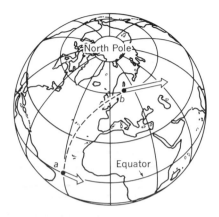

FIG. 5–4
An object initially at rest at the equator acquires a westerly velocity component as it moves poleward, to conserve its angular momentum.

radius, or about 4000 miles. The object is then given a "push" which starts it moving poleward. To conserve its angular momentum, it would develop an increasingly high west-to-east velocity, since its distance from the earth's axis would be decreasing. By the time the object reached 60° N, the latitude at which the distance from the axis had reached 2000 miles (one-half the equatorial figure) the west-to-east velocity theoretically would have doubled to 2000 miles/hour. Conversely, an object originally at the pole would acquire an east-to-west velocity as it moved equatorward, for the same reasons.

Coriolis Force

Experiments using a turntable and spring-loaded marble guns are useful in showing what effect rotation of the surface has on bodies rolling over a flat surface. Refer to Fig. 5–5. Let the turntable rotate in a counterclockwise sense; cock the spring guns with the same tension, thus giving each ball the same initial velocity; aim them at each other, and arrange to fire them simultaneously without disturbing the rotation. Four ideal-

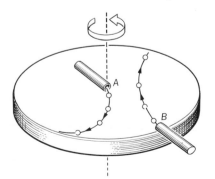

FIG. 5–5
Rotating turntable enables simulation of motion over rotating earth.

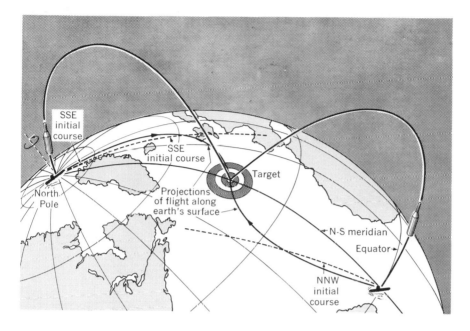

FIG. 5–6
Polaris submarine on the equator must launch a rocket on
NNW course to hit a target on the dateline at 45° N latitude.
A submarine at the North Pole must use SSE course.

ized "snapshot views" show what happens. *Neither* ball hits the target.
The ball from *A* appears to drift off to the right along the line from
A to *B*, *as judged by an observer on the turntable* who stands with his
back to the direction of motion. The ball from *B* appears likewise to
drift off to the right along the line from *B* to *A*. One might say that the
motion of each of the balls appeared to an observer on the table as
though a force were acting on them at right angles to their direction of
motion, pulling them away from a straight-line path. This effect is called
the *Coriolis force.*

The earth's surface looks something like a flat turntable from a great
distance over the North Pole. But, of course, this is an illusion, and the
hemispherical shape introduces additional complications in the motion
over its surface.

It is possible to enlarge the spring-gun example, in thought, to rockets
loaded with warheads. Visualize, as in Fig. 5–6, two Polaris submarines
on maneuver, one at rest in a break in the surface ice at the North Pole,
and the other on the equator, both firing at a target halfway between

FIG. 5–7
Streak diagram of circulation in rotating-dishpan experiment, and corresponding stream lines showing centers of cyclonic (C) and anticyclonic (A) eddies. Trough lines are dashed. After D. Fultz, *Meteorological Monographs* **14**, December 1959.

them, for example, on the date line at 180° W longitude. On what course should the missiles be launched to hit the target? It should be clear from the previous example that neither missile would impact on the target area if it were launched on a course which was directly south and north respectively. What sort of compensation would have to be made? The polar missile would have to be launched on a course somewhat to the SSE, and the equatorial missile would have to be launched on a course somewhat to the NNW. (See if you can apply this reasoning to a Southern-Hemisphere situation.)

Another interesting and informative turntable experiment of a somewhat more sophisticated nature involves a flat-bottomed dishpan arranged so that it can be heated along the edge and cooled at the center, simulating the equator and pole respectively. See Fig. 5–7. An inch or so of water is placed in the pan. A few drops of dye make flow patterns visible. The Hadley cell is set up when the center is cooler than the perimeter, and when the dishpan is still. So long as the turntable rotates less than about two revolutions/minute the pattern remains simple. At higher speeds the simple circulation breaks up into a series of big eddies fed by little eddies, analogous to the eddy patterns encountered in the real atmosphere.

Meteorology has several "chicken-versus-egg" questions. One is: Does a particular pressure distribution produce a wind system, or does a particular wind system produce a corresponding pressure distribution? The traditional approach has been to assume a pressure field and deduce the wind field which corresponds to it, though the other approach could be used as well. The wind field could be assumed and the corresponding pressure field could be deduced from it. Perhaps this is the same sort of question the physicist encounters when he asks whether force is a more fundamental concept than mass. The point is arguable, but Newton's second law of motion, written as $F = ma$, is valid whichever may be the case.

Geostrophic Wind

We will be traditionalists and assume the pressure field; i.e., we will assume that the pressure is greater in one location than it is in another. We will then ask what happens to a small mass of air which, for lack of a better term, we shall call a "blob." Let it be initially at rest. The blob will experience a force which accelerates it from higher toward lower pressure, in the same way and for the same reason that water flows downhill. But immediately as the blob starts to move over its rotating earth platform it appears, to an earth-bound observer, to be pulled to the right with a force proportional to its speed. This is the Coriolis force. The force also varies according to latitude, reaching a maximum at the pole and dropping to zero at the equator (actually the force is proportional to the *sine* of the latitude). Figure 5–8 shows "time-lapse" views of what happens to our blob. Finally the Coriolis force becomes so large, because of the continued acceleration and resultant increased speed, that it exactly counterbalances the force due to the pressure field. Then, contradictory as it may seem at first, the blob is acted upon by *no net force* and, according to the laws of motion, will continue to move at uniform speed in a straight line, which happens to be parallel to the isobars. The latitude factor means that for a given spacing, the wind will move faster in low latitudes than it will in higher latitudes.

The drag due to surface friction introduces an additional force. This decreases the speed, and hence the Coriolis force, and the result is an airdrift across the isobars toward lower pressure. The effect of surface friction becomes negligible above 2500–3500 feet, at which level we establish what is called the *geostrophic wind*. The equation of the geostrophic wind is written

$$-\frac{1}{\rho}\frac{\Delta p}{\Delta x} = 2\,\omega v \sin \phi,$$

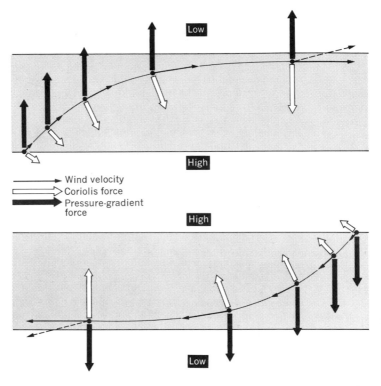

FIG. 5–8
Development of geostrophic wind from rest condition. Surface friction
causes a cross-isobar flow toward low pressure.

where $\Delta p/\Delta x$ is the *pressure gradient* (the rate at which pressure decreases with distance measured perpendicular to the isobars), ρ is the
air density, v is the wind speed, ω is the angular speed of the earth
about its axis, ϕ is the latitude. We see that the speed of the wind, for
a given latitude, is inversely proportional to the spacing of the isobars;
i.e., the closer the isobars are spaced, the higher the wind speed.

Gradient Wind

What happens when the isobars are no longer straight lines but are
curved? The laws of motion say that a force must be exerted on any
object to make it change its direction of motion as well as its straight-
line speed. As with the rock tied to the string, the central force must
be at right angles inward toward the center of motion. But the blob of
air has no string attached to it to provide the force. Therefore, the force

must be supplied by the pressure gradient. To simplify our reasoning, we assume circular isobars with equidistant spacing; i.e., the pressure gradient is everywhere the same. First we will look at the case of air motion about a low-pressure center, a *low,* as shown in Fig. 5–9(a). Here we see that the centripetal force and the pressure-gradient force are in the same direction. Remembering that the pressure-gradient force is that given through the particular pressure distribution, we can see that, when the pressure-gradient force is greater than the Coriolis force, by an amount equal to the value of the centripetal force necessary to change the direction of the blob, the blob will move uniformly along the curved isobars. If the blob is to move in a tight circle, the centripetal force is correspondingly greater than if the curvature of the path is very slight.

In the case of air motion about a high-pressure center, or a *high,* as shown in Fig. 5–9(b), the centripetal force and the pressure-gradient force are in opposite directions. Here the Coriolis force is greater than the pressure-gradient force, and the difference is accounted for once again by the value of the centripetal force necessary to change the direction of the blob.

The practical result of these two cases is the following: If we still assume constant isobaric spacing at a constant latitude, the blob will move more slowly around a low than it will around a high. Actually, pressure gradients tend to be greater in low's than in high's. High wind speeds are thus associated with low-pressure systems more frequently than they are with high-pressure systems.

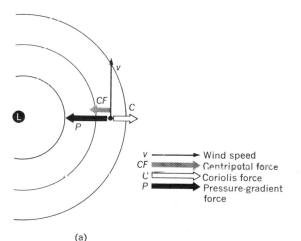

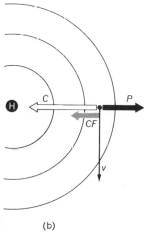

v	Wind speed
CF	Centripetal force
C	Coriolis force
P	Pressure-gradient force

(a)

(b)

FIG. 5–9
Development of gradient wind.

Stating the same problem for the case of *constant wind speed,* we can say that, in comparison with the spacing for flow in a straight line, the isobars can be spaced farther apart when the wind is making a right-hand turn, and must be closer together when it is making a left-hand turn.

In the last few paragraphs we spelled out the physical basis for one of the most ancient and famous empirical rules of meteorology: *Buys Ballot's law.* This states that if an observer stands with his back to the wind in the Northern Hemisphere, high pressure will be to his right and low pressure to his left. Conversely, if he is in the Southern Hemisphere, high pressure will be to his left and low pressure to his right.

We are now prepared to go back to Figs. 3–9 and 3–10, which show the mean pressure distribution in January and July, and from this discern the mean wind circulation. The northeast winds which blow out of the south side of the large high-pressure centers in the major oceans are called *trade winds.* We note that the pressure gradient on the south side of these high's is much stronger in July than in January. As expected, the trade winds are much stronger in summer than in winter. In contrast, the pressure gradients are much stronger on the north side of the high's in winter than summer. The *prevailing westerlies* are much stronger in winter than in summer. These two wind streams are the principal elements of the low-level general circulation of the earth's atmosphere which can be seen on a global surface chart.

Upper-Level Winds

We now raise the question of what happens to this picture of pressure and wind distribution as we go aloft into the middle troposphere, i.e., to the levels where the barometric pressure is about half its sea-level value, or 500 millibars.

We must think again about the effect of temperature on pressure and density. The meteorologist expresses this in terms of a relation called the *hydrostatic equation,* which can be written

in which Δp is the change in pressure, Δz is the change in elevation, g is the acceleration due to gravity, and ρ is the density. This simply says that the decrease of pressure with altitude is proportional to the density. Since the density of the air is relatively great when the temperature is cold (and vice versa), we might expect the pressure to drop most rapidly with respect to altitude in high latitudes in the winter season.

In other words 500-millibar pressure should be encountered at a lower elevation near the poles than near the equator.

If we were now to consider a hypothetical surface to be defined by the condition that the pressure is 500 millibars at all places on it, such a surface would slope down poleward from its highest value in the Tropics. Furthermore, it should slope most rapidly in the winter season, in comparison to the summer.

Figures 3–11 and 3–12 show mean monthly charts of the height of the 500-millibar surface in January and July. The solid lines are contours of equal heights; i.e., at any place along a particular line the height of this pressure surface is the same. The spacing of the contour lines gives an indication of the slope of the surface which contains the 500-millibar pressure, in the sense that close spacing represents a steeply sloping surface. We note that in the winter the surface dips to 16,000 feet, while in the summer its lowest level is about 18,000 feet.

We can get a sense of the circulation of the middle troposphere by analyzing these contour charts much as we analyzed the surface-pressure charts. Buys Ballot's law still holds, but in the following form: If one stands with his back to the wind, high contours are to the right and low contours to the left. Also valid is the relation between closeness of the spacing of the contour lines and the wind strength. Therefore Fig. 3–11 tells us that the outstanding feature of the middle troposphere is a vast whirl of westerly winds (air which is rotating about the earth's axis faster than the earth's surface is moving). Not shown on these charts is a counterequatorial easterly current which is stronger in summer than winter, whereas the westerly current is stronger in winter than summer.

Focusing our attention on a particular contour line, we note that it meanders north and south as we follow it around the globe. Or, if we examine it with respect to a given latitude circle, it undulates up and down. The meteorologist sees much meaning in these meandering wave motions in the circular westerly flow pattern. The length of the waves and their amplitude vary with the circumstances, but a figure which can be used for orientation is 60 degrees in longitude for the wavelength, and 5 to 10 degrees in latitude for the amplitude. These waves have a significant bearing on surface-weather patterns.

When one studies them day after day, one finds that waves of short wavelength and small amplitude move eastward with reasonable speeds; waves of longer wavelength and large amplitude move very slowly, remain stationary, or sometimes even move slowly *westward* (retrogress).

These waves are reflections (or are they the cause?) of surface activity. The waves of short wavelength and small amplitude (Fig. 5–10) are

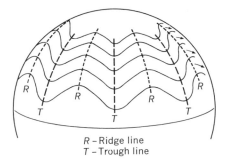

R – Ridge line
T – Trough line

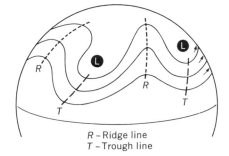

R – Ridge line
T – Trough line

FIG. 5–10
Small-amplitude waves in westerly wind
stream. Right-hand turning occurs at
the ridges; left-hand turning occurs
through the troughs.

FIG. 5–11
Large-amplitude, stationary waves in
westerly air stream.

associated with fast-moving and shallow depressions which move primarily from west to east. The waves of long wavelength and large
amplitude (Fig. 5–11) are associated with a breakdown of the normal
west-east pattern of storm tracks to a different pattern consisting of
strong intrusions of cold air far southward and warm air far northward.
This pattern explains why frosts nip the citrus-tree blooms in one
geographical section while at the same time in another longitude the
snow melts from the ski slopes.

The forecaster depends on the upper-air flow pattern, for he knows
that it provides him with significant weather tips. Along and to the east
of the line of maximum right-hand turning, a line which he calls a *ridge,*
he knows that the air tends to sink. Because of the compressional warming due to the gentle descent of the air into levels of higher pressure,
cloudiness is inhibited. On the other hand, along and to the east of the
line of maximum left-hand turning, called a *trough,* the reverse is true.
Air which is caused to rise cools as it expands in the regions of lower
pressure. As a result of the cooling, cloudiness and precipitation are
favored.

The temperature field in the middle troposphere has a similar pattern
to the contours of the 500-millibar pressure surface. Isotherms tend to
be oriented in a west-east line around cold temperatures at the poles and
warm temperatures in the Tropics. Like the contours, the isotherms tend
to have a sinuous, wavy motion. When a particular isotherm dips well
toward the south, there has been a southward intrusion of cold air; when
it moves well to the north, there has been a northward intrusion of warm
air. We can also speak of troughs and ridges in the temperature field.
The wave patterns in the temperature and contour fields are related, but

not superimposed one on the other. The trough and ridge lines in the temperature field tend to be displaced somewhat westward of the trough and ridge lines in the contour field. The presence of cold air aloft in the general region where the air is making a left-hand turn means instability in the mass. This encourages the development of cumulus-type clouds and showery weather. The presence of warm air aloft where the air stream is making a right-hand turn suggests stability in the air mass. In regions where the air is ascending, it produces layer clouds, and in regions where the air is descending, it inhibits cloud forms of any sort.

Jet Stream

The westerly flow pattern in the middle troposphere has a special feature referred to as the *jet stream*. This special feature remained unknown until it was encountered in the early 1940's by B-24 bombers making high-level runs from the east on Tokyo during World War II. Some of

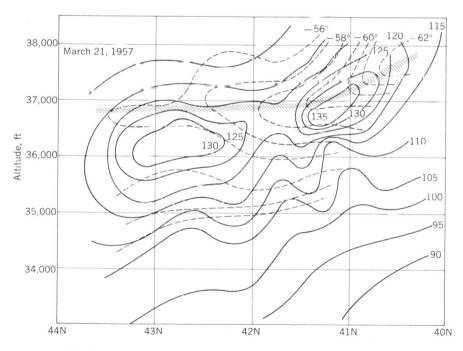

FIG. 5–12
Core of Jet Stream along a N–S section. The solid lines are isotachs, or lines of equal velocity in knots. The barred line is the tropopause. The dashed lines are centigrade isotherms. Note the increase in temperature above the tropopause.

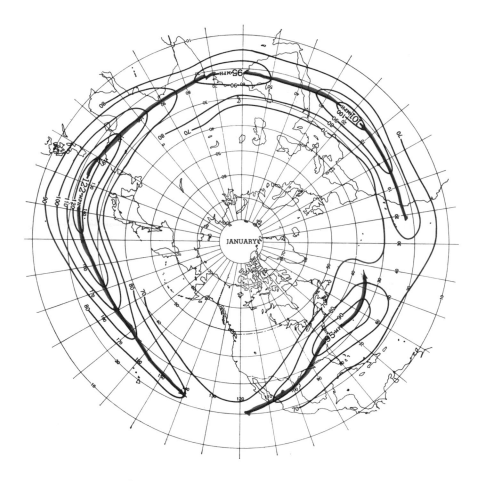

FIG. 5–13
Jet Stream in winter as seen from far above the North Pole. Isotachs in mph.
From Sverre Petterssen, *Introduction to Meteorology*, 2nd ed., New York:
McGraw-Hill, 1958, by permission.

the aircraft encountered narrow currents of wind so strong that they could make no ground speed at all. The first reports were attributed to navigational error. Meteorologists finally realized, as additional reports came into the briefing offices, that a new phenomenon had been discovered. Over two decades have now passed. Based on analysis of much Raob and Rawin data, and inflight reports from high-flying aircraft which both accidentally and intentionally encountered the jet stream, meteorologists have now gained a reasonable understanding of its cause and behavior, which we now summarize.

One encounters the jet stream just under a tropopause which has been lowered following an equatorward intrusion of the surface polar front. When a cross-section diagram of westerly wind velocities is prepared along a particular longitude line, as in Fig. 5–12, one finds this "core" of extremely high westerly wind velocities which reach 150 knots routinely, and sometimes are reported as high as 250 knots. This is a narrow core which has a north-south extent of perhaps 200 miles and a vertical extent of 1 mile. Lines of equal velocity, called *isotacns*, are used to portray the jet-stream cross section. In the example shown, consisting of actual flight information taken from Project Jet Stream, it is instructive to note the behavior of temperature with respect to altitude along the different latitude lines. The coldest temperatures establish the tropopause. Above this level in the stratosphere there is a temperature inversion; i.e., the temperature rises with elevation. Underneath, the temperature drops rapidly with elevation up to the tropopause. Corresponding to this region of rapid temperature change, the westerly winds increase rapidly to a high maximum; hence the word "core." Generally speaking, the wind speed of the core diminishes most rapidly to the north, dropping by 30–60 knots in 60 miles, while to the south the rate of decrease is about half that value.

The jet stream pattern as seen from a hypothetical meteorological satellite hovering over the North Pole might be something like that shown in Fig. 5–13.

Since our object in this chapter has been to show what results from the lack of thermal balance over the face of the globe, we have given primary attention to the major large-scale features of the atmosphere in motion. Before closing we must mention briefly three other features.

Smaller-Scale Circulations

The first of these is the *monsoonal circulation.* This takes place on a continent-size space scale and is a seasonal phenomenon. Referring back to Figs. 3–9 and 3–10, we see that during the winter the eastern part of the Asian continent is covered by a massive thermal high pressure centered in Siberia, whereas in the summer this vanishes and is replaced by an equally extensive thermal low-pressure area. As a result, in the winter, cold dry air pours from the continent over all of southeast Asia. This vast movement of air is called the *northeast monsoon* and provides the fair-weather period for this entire region. In the summer months the flow reverses direction. In this period hot, moisture-packed air from the Indian Ocean pushes northeastward over India, Southeast Asia, and the Philippines, bringing with it extensive cloudiness and rain which becomes torrential when the air encounters any orographic barrier. This is called the *southwest monsoon.*

Other continents, for example Africa, have monsoonal circulations, but nowhere are they so extensive as the one described.

Lest we lose sight of the physical cause of this great migration of air, we should remember that this is primarily a manifestation of the large difference between the heat-holding capacities of soil and water. The land temperature rises more rapidly than the water temperature in the summer. Thus the air over the land is warmed, and the thermal low is induced. In the winter the temperature of the soil drops more rapidly than that of the water, as a consequence of the outflow of terrestrial radiation. As the surface becomes cold, the air over it becomes cold and dense, and the thermal high gradually establishes itself.

This leads us to a description of the second circulation feature, the *land-and-sea breeze*. Here, precisely the same sequence of events occurs, but on a diurnal time scale. During the afternoon the air is heated over the warm land, rises, and is replaced by heavier, cool air flowing landward from the sea. During the early morning hours the cold dense air over the land glides seaward, replacing the warmer air over the sea.

The third circulation feature is called the *mountain-and-valley breeze.* During the night, cold dense air seeps down from the exposed mountain slopes into the valley. During the afternoon, the air at the same elevation over the valley is colder than near the mountain, because the heating of the air is related to its closeness to the land surface. As a consequence, the air along the mountain slope will rise and be replaced by the cooler air from below. More extensive coverage of these three patterns can be found in any standard text on climatology.

Knowing the main features of atmospheric motion, we are now prepared to examine in more detail the cyclonic eddy which is referred to as the *extratropical wave cyclone*.

CHAPTER 6

**The
Wave
Cyclone**

*We begin by developing the concept of an air
mass. Polar continental and equatorial maritime
types are defined. Then we discuss the polar
front, which is the origin of the discontinuity
bounding polar and tropical air masses. This
leads to a description and definition of cold front
and warm front. The Bjerknes wave-cyclone
model is introduced, and a family of cyclones,
each in a different stage of development, is
described. Finally, we use a "cut-out" cross-
section diagram to illustrate the characteristics
of fronts in terms of slope, resulting cloud
forms, and precipitation patterns.*

AIR MASSES

Air which remains for days or weeks over a specific portion of the earth's surface will gradually acquire the characteristics of that surface. If the surface is warm and moist, the air will become warm and humid; if the surface is hot and dry, the air will become hot and arid; if the surface is very cold and snow-covered, the air will become very cold and dry (because cold air can hold very little moisture); and so on. If the surface area under consideration is quite large, ranging upward of, say, ten thousand square miles, the body of air is referred to as an *air mass*. An air mass is a large mass of air which has acquired homogeneous (evenly distributed) values of temperature and moisture, level for level.

Air which moves slowly westward for thousands of miles under the driving influence of one of the semipermanent oceanic anticyclones will gradually acquire in the low levels the characteristic temperature of the tropical ocean. By the time the air has reached the western extremity of the ocean basin, the warmth and moisture will have penetrated to considerable heights as a result of the turbulent mixing and convection. Such air is designated as an *equatorial maritime air mass*.

At the other extreme, winter air frequently remains relatively stagnant over the snow-covered wastes of Siberia and/or Canada. During the long nights the ground becomes extremely cold because of the great excess of outgoing terrestrial radiation over incoming solar radiation. By conduction (or contact cooling) the air lying over this surface becomes very cold and dry. Such air is designated as a *polar continental air mass*. As the air becomes colder it also becomes more dense and is pulled earthward with a greater force. As a consequence the surface air pressure gradually increases in this region as contrasted with surrounding regions, and an anticyclonic (clockwise) circulation develops.

THE POLAR FRONT

Finally the great mass of cold air can no longer maintain its stationary position and starts to move slowly southward. When the frigid northeasterly winds on its forward side encounter the warm and moist northward-moving air from the Tropics, the stage is set for a battle of the elements. This is shown in Fig. 6–1. The battle line, or demarcation between the two air masses, is known as the *polar front*. This front is a surface across which the properties of temperature and moisture content change abruptly. The plane slopes poleward from its intersection with the surface. In some regions along the front the cold, dense air surges equatorward, causing the warm air to be forced aloft over its sloping surface. This portion of the polar front is known as a *cold front*. Cold front is formally defined as *a surface intersection of a plane of discontinuity along which cold, dry air is displacing warm, moist air.* In other portions of the polar front the cold air retreats northward and the warm air advances over it. This portion is known as a *warm front.* A *warm front is the surface intersection of a plane of discontinuity along which warm air replaces and advances over a retreating cold air mass.*

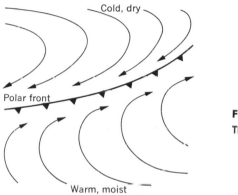

FIG. 6–1
The polar front.

The slope of the cold front is steeper than that of the warm front, as seen in Fig. 6–2. Average values respectively are 1 mile rise to 75 miles along the horizontal ($\frac{1}{75}$), and 1 mile rise to 250 miles along the horizontal ($\frac{1}{250}$).

One can get a crude sense of the way the air motion over the earth's surface influences the slope of the discontinuity by holding a common lead pencil (eraser down) obliquely on a table. When one *pushes* the pencil ahead the frictional drag between the table and the eraser tends to make the slope of the pencil increase. Conversely, when the pencil is

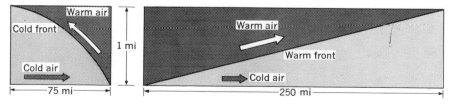

FIG. 6–2
Relative slopes of cold and warm fronts.

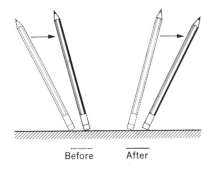

Before   After

FIG. 6–3
The effect of surface friction on the
slope of fronts.

pulled the frictional drag causes the slope to decrease. These two cases
are shown in Fig. 6–3.

The region of the polar front is a region of concentration of potential
energy. The mechanism nature has produced for the dissipation of this
energy is the extratropical cyclone. This storm is born as a wave on the
front; it grows in amplitude and eventually dissipates in somewhat the
same sequence as an ocean wave: on approaching a beach, it increases
steeply in amplitude as it "feels the bottom," crests, topples, and finally
breaks. (The reader should be warned that the atmospheric wave is
much more difficult to conceptualize than the water wave.)

THE WAVE CYCLONE

One of the most influential meteorological papers ever written was
titled "On The Structure of Moving Cyclones." Its author was J. Bjerknes,
a Norwegian, and it appeared in *Geofysiske Publikationer*, Vol. 1, No. 2
(Oslo, 1919). In its brief eight pages Bjerknes proposed a model for the
migratory cyclone which has been used with great success by meteorologists the world over for half a century. In this model we find his crude
"steering line" replaced by the warm front, and his "squall line" replaced
by the cold front.

Bjerknes related his cold front and warm front to each other in the
form of a wave which increased in amplitude with respect to time. His
classic diagram of the wave cyclone is shown in Fig. 6–4. In the same
year (1919) other scientists of the Norwegian "Bergen" school refined
Bjerknes' basic ideas, connecting a series of fronts associated with different storms to form a "family" of cyclones, or waves, on this polar front.

A "snapshot" view of a family of wave cyclones in various stages of
development is shown in Fig. 6–5. Note that high-pressure areas lie
both to the south and the north. Warm air is fed northward around the
western periphery of the vast oceanic, semipermanent anticyclone. Cold

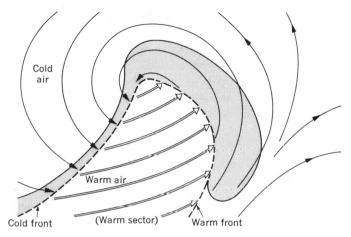

FIG. 6–4
J. Bjerknes' model of wave cyclone.

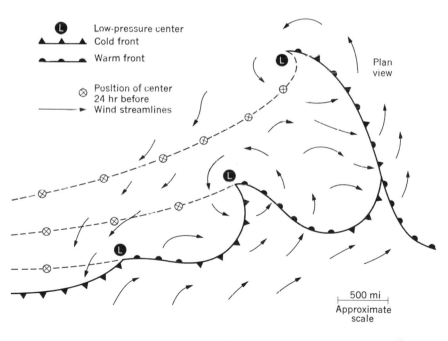

FIG. 6–5
A family of three wave cyclones in different stages of development. The track of each center is successively closer to the equator.

much like on page 107. b.

air is fed southward from the polar anticyclone which had its origin in the snow-covered Arctic. Between the two streams lies the polar front.

Does this initiation of the wave disturbance along the front by the plunging of the cold air into the warm air at some place along the front cause the lowering of pressure noted to occur at the apex of the wave, or does some other factor, perhaps at higher elevation, initiate the lowering of pressure which starts the wave development along the front? This is another "chicken-versus-egg" question which has not been resolved. Suffice it to say at this point that the question is not a simple one, or it would have been resolved years ago.

As the amplitude of the wave increases, the atmospheric pressure at the apex continues to drop because of outflow at upper levels over this region. This produces an increased pressure gradient, and consequently the winds will be stronger as the isobars are closer together. As the winds increase the general ascent of air throughout the cyclonic region increases, compensating for more active cross-isobar flow toward low pressure in low levels. The activity of the fronts also increases as the cold air pushes vigorously equatorward behind the cold front, and the warm air ascends the gentle warm frontal slope.

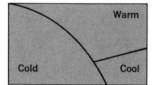

Cold-front occlusion

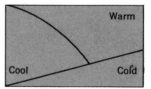

Warm-front occlusion

FIG. 6–6
Cold- and warm-front occlusions.

Because of the sluggishness of the cold air under the warm frontal surface, the cold front closes in on the warm front as the amplitude of the wave increases. As the cold front reaches the warm front, surface warm-sector air between the fronts is lifted aloft. This lifting aloft of the warm air is called *occlusion*. Since the cold air *behind* the cold front and the cold air *under* the warm frontal surface have had different life histories, and therefore possess different properties, there are two different kinds of occluded fronts. When the *colder* air behind the cold front undercuts the *cold* air under the warm front, we have a *cold-front occlusion* with an upper warm front. Or, when the *cold* air behind the cold front rides over the *colder* air under the warm front, we have a *warm-front occlusion* with an upper cold front, as shown in Fig. 6–6.

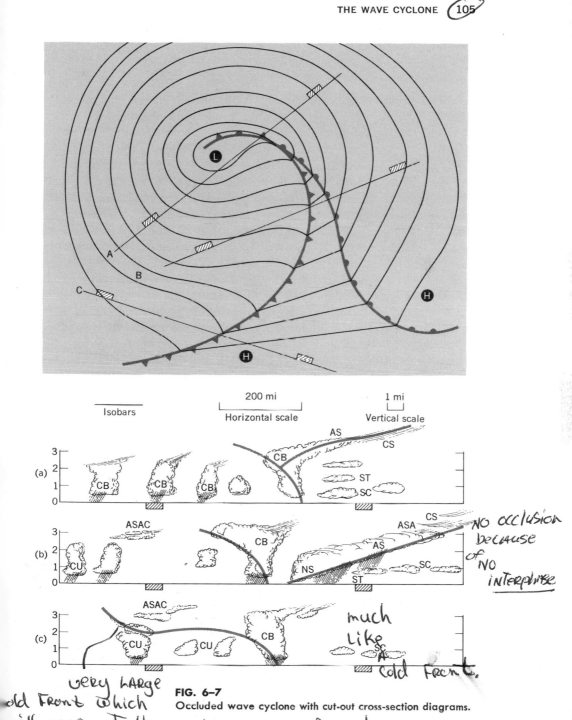

NO OCCLUSION
because
of NO
interphase

much
Like
cold front.

FIG. 6–7
Occluded wave cyclone with cut-out cross-section diagrams.

very LARGE
old Front which
will move out the weaker warm front

In Chapter 1 we described a sequence of clouds which an observer on an oceanic weather ship might have seen as an extratropical cyclone passed his station. We now relate this more specifically to an idealized occluded frontal storm through a series of cross-sectional analyses. If a quarter section were cut out of an orange, one could look in cross section at the skin. We will in effect be doing this except that our "cut" of the "earth orange" will only be as deep as the skin, namely, the atmosphere.

Figure 6–7 shows an active occluded front. It is instructive to cut out the three cross sections in the figure and insert them on the plan view of the storm represented on the surface chart. The reader should note that two different scales of distance are employed for the horizontal and vertical. If the same scale were used for both, the fronts would be scarcely distinguishable from the horizontal base line. In other words, the fronts have extremely shallow true-scale slopes. We note several characteristics. One is that the cloud forms at the cold and warm fronts are very different. In the case of the former the snowplow effect of the steep cold front causes a sudden upthrust of the warm air. This tends to set off convective clouds of the cumulonimbus type, which produce heavy showery precipitation of relatively short duration. In contrast, the slow upglide of the warm air over the gently sloping warm front produces layers of sheet clouds at all levels: high, middle, and low. Continuous rain tends to fall from warm-front clouds. In the case of the occluded front the layer clouds merge into the heap clouds and the continuous rain merges into the heavy showers with no break. Some of the severest weather in the wave cyclone is found near the point of occlusion.

The approach and passage of the cold front is marked (on the average) by the following changes in the meteorological variables: a steady drop in *pressure* followed by a rapid rise; southwesterly *winds* increasing in speed and suddenly shifting to fresh northwesterly; warm *temperatures* with high *humidity* suddenly dropping and becoming less humid; showers or squalls from a line of cumulus and/or cumulonimbus *clouds* followed by clearing skies.

The passage of the warm front is marked by the following changes: a slow drop in pressure becoming steady; southeasterly winds changing to southwesterly; cool temperatures increasing to warm; humidities remaining rather high; continuous rain from nimbostratus cloud diminishing and ceasing.

Since this is an idealized model, there will be local variations in which the sequence of events does not quite jibe with the ideal. However, it has been found that the wave-cyclone picture visualized nearly half a century ago by Bjerknes is a very useful model of what really happens

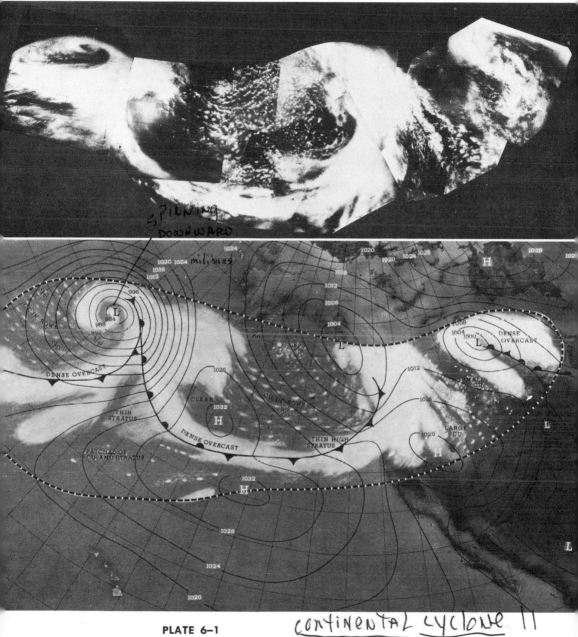

PLATE 6-1

Comparison of Tiros cloud pattern and frontal positions on an analyzed weather chart. Photo courtesy U.S. Weather Bureau.

in nature, and it is still the basic feature of the surface-weather chart drawn in forecasting offices the world over.

A dramatic test, conducted three weeks after Tiros I was launched, was carried out by Tor Bergeron, a famous Swedish contemporary of Bjerknes. Bergeron constructed a cloud map which the Bjerknes model predicted should be associated with an actual series of waves which had developed along the polar front. This was then compared with a nephanalysis (cloud map) based on the Tiros photographs made of this frontal system. An excellent correlation was found between the two sets of pictures. Plate 6-1 illustrates a typically high correlation.

The conclusions meteorologists have drawn, after viewing many Tiros cloud maps, is that the atmospheric processes do follow the Bjerknes model, but yield more complex patterns than are predicted by the model.

CHAPTER 7

**Water,
Dirty Air,
and
Cloud
Chambers**

*As an approach to the formation of the water
droplets which make up clouds, we review the
structure of matter. Among the many atoms,
oxygen and hydrogen are of special concern, for
together they form the water molecule, which
we describe. Hydrogen bonding is explained
and shown to be particularly important between
adjacent water molecules. Next we use our
knowledge of hydrogen bonding to describe
the solid, liquid, and gaseous states of matter.
The unusually large latent heats of fusion and
vaporization and specific heats of water
are discussed. This leads to the concept of
the ocean as an "energy bank." After describing the composition of air we discuss the
several mechanisms by which foreign matter
is added to it: frictional rubbing of the wind
over the surface, bursting of air bubbles at the
surface of the sea, volcanic eruption, combustion,
and chemical reactions. We trace the history
of measurement of the amount of "dirtiness"
in the atmosphere, and show how a great
number of these foreign particles serve as nuclei
on which cloud particles form.*

In the first chapter the subject of clouds was approached from an observational point of view. In this chapter we deal with the same subject, but this time from a physical point of view. Here we are not concerned with description so much as with reaching an understanding of the conditions nature places on cloud formation.

Since clouds are formed of myriads of water droplets and/or ice crystals so tiny that each can scarcely be seen by the naked eye, our first concern will be the nature of water itself. The chances are that the commonness of water has obscured the fact that it is a very unusual substance. To understand the reason for the unusual properties of water we must look beyond the structure of the water molecule to the nature of the component elements, hydrogen and oxygen.

NATURE OF WATER

Periodic Table of Elements

Every element is composed of a tiny, dense, central nucleus made up of protons, carrying the elementary positive charge, and neutrons, which are electrically neutral. One finds equal numbers of negatively charged "particles" called electrons, distributed in shells, whirling at fantastic speeds around the nucleus. (The term "shell" is understood to mean regions in space where the electrons are most likely to be found.) More specifically, the arrangement of the electrons in the shell structure is governed by a principle known as the *exclusion principle,* formulated by the physicist Wolfgang Pauli. This states, in layman's language, that no two electrons of a particular atom can have precisely the same set of properties. (Since the set of properties referred to must be expressed in the mathematical language of quantum mechanics, we let the statement stand with no elaboration and refer the curious reader to such popular texts in physics as Max Born's *The Restless Universe.*)

At the present time 103 different elements have been identified. This means that there are 103 different atomic nuclei (in terms of proton numbers). There are also 103 different electron-distribution patterns, which are precisely dictated by the laws of quantum physics.

From this emerges all the particularity and individuality one finds in nature, both animate and inanimate. The orderly way in which the electron structure is built up is best illustrated by Table 7–1. We have shown only the first group of elements in our table, but this is sufficient to indicate the pattern of development. One notes that the first shell (the K-shell) becomes filled with 2 electrons, the second (the L-shell) with 8 electrons, the third (the M-shell) with 18 electrons, the fourth (the

TABLE 7–1

The pattern of electron structure illustrated by the first group of elements

Shell			K	L		M			N			
Quantum numbers		n,1	1,0	2,0	2,1	3,0	3,1	3,2	4,0	4,1	4,2	4,3
Element		Atomic number										
Hydrogen	H	1	1	—	—							
*Helium	He	2	2	—	—							
Lithium	Li	3	2	1	—							
Berrylium	Be	4	2	2	—							
Boron	B	5	2	2	1							
Carbon	C	6	2	2	2							
Nitrogen	N	7	2	2	3							
Oxygen	O	8	2	2	4							
Fluorine	F	9	2	2	5							
*Neon	Ne	10	2	2	6							
Sodium	Na	11	2	2	6	1						
Magnesium	Mg	12	2	2	6	2						

N-shell) with 32 electrons, the fifth (the O-shell) with 54 electrons, and the sixth (the P-shell) with 86 electrons. One of the cardinal rules of nature is that, all other factors being equal, configurations of minimum energy will be assumed. This means, in the context of this discussion, that the innermost shells will be the first filled.

Chemical characteristics emerge naturally from the table. For instance, one would expect that elements with completely filled shells would be inert and would not react with other elements. And so it is. Helium and neon (*asterisked in the table*), argon, kryton, xenon, and radon are known as the noble gases because they do not interact. In a sense they are the "have-nations" of the atomic world. They have all the electrons they want or need. Therefore they do not seek to attain more or get rid of any electrons. They are self-sufficient. But these are the exception rather than the rule, in the atomic world as in the world of nations. There are more "have-nots" than "haves." Just as nations strive to acquire what they need to satisfy their wants, or to relieve internal tensions by reducing their wants, atoms lacking filled electron shells strive actively to complete their shells by acquiring electrons, and atoms with new shells barely filled tend to balance themselves by relinquishing these electrons, aiming always toward the stability of an inert gas. These enterprises require the "have-nots" to enter into cooperative arrangements with other atoms. Such arrangements are molecules. We now focus our attention on one particular molecule: water, or H_2O.

Water Molecule

Each of the elements combining to form water exists independently in molecules containing two atoms (H_2, O_2) held together by forces called *covalent bonds.* In the case of hydrogen each nucleus is held (bonded) close to the other by the attractive force resulting from the fact that each atom shares its electron with the other, thus making an electron pair. Chemist Linus Pauling suggests the analogy of two steel balls (the nuclei) vulcanized into a tough piece of rubber (the electrons) which surrounds them and bonds them together. In the case of oxygen the molecule is held together by a single covalent bond, leaving two unpaired electrons.

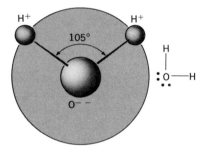

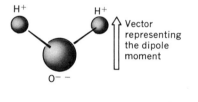

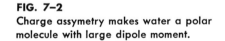

FIG. 7–1
Water molecule and chemical designation.

FIG. 7–2
Charge assymetry makes water a polar molecule with large dipole moment.

This sharing of the electrons in H_2 and O_2 causes an unevenness in the distribution of the positive and negative charges within each molecule. This determines the "Mickey Mouse" shape of the water molecule. Figure 7–1 is a schematic representation of one of the two H_2O molecules resulting from the combination of $2H_2$ and O_2. The equilibrium position taken by the two hydrogen atoms places them 0.95 angstrom units (1 angstrom = 10^{-10} meter) from the oxygen nucleus, and separates them from one another by an angle of 105 degrees. In effect the water molecule can be described as a doubly charged oxygen ion (O^{--}) with two hydrogen ions (H^+) attached to it. This fact, that the centers of negative and positive charge do not coincide, means that the water molecule is one of a class called *polar molecules.* Such molecules have a tendency to orient themselves in line with an electric field. See Fig. 7–2. The magnitude of the charge separation is called the *dipole moment,* and in a water molecule the separation is relatively great. This is expressed in technical language by saying that the dielectric constant of water is 80 (compared to 1 for a vacuum), which means that two electric charges will attract or repel each other only 1/80 as strongly in water as in a vacuum. This is an important consideration in the remarkable dissolving of water, because of which it is called the universal solvent. But there is another important force, referred to as the *hydrogen bond.*

Hydrogen Bond and States of Matter

The hydrogen bond is a bond between individual molecules whose inward integrity is maintained by strong covalent bonds. Water provides an example. By means of the hydrogen bond, water molecules are joined together (bonded) in a community of rare tightness and continuity of structure. This bonding force is electrostatic in nature and exists between the exposed positive (proton) center of a hydrogen nucleus and any single, unpaired, electron of another (water) molecule. Since each oxygen atom in the water molecule happens to have two such unpaired electrons, each water molecule can form four hydrogen bonds.

When all four bonds, each at an angle of 105 degrees to the other, are firmly established between all the water molecules in a particular mass of water, the molecules become fixed in a certain geometrical relation to each other and can do no more than vibrate around the fixed equilibrium points. The water assumes the characteristics of a *solid,* is said to have frozen, and (of course) is called ice. The detailed structure of ice will be discussed in the next chapter in conjunction with the precipitation problem. This subject will be pursued no further here.

When the four bonds are not firmly established but are continually being formed and broken, it is possible for the water substance to take on the shape of its container and *flow.* This is the so-called *liquid state.*

When all the hydrogen bonds are broken and each molecule is an individual, unattached to others, the water substance is in the gaseous state and the term *water vapor* is applied to it.

Here, then, are the three states of matter. One of the peculiarities, and we might say a very fortuitous peculiarity, of this planet is that its distance from the sun is such that, for water, all three states of matter can coexist. Within the range of temperatures experienced on earth we find much water locked up in the solid state, a vast amount present in the liquid state in the oceans, seas, lakes, and rivers, and a very small but exceedingly important fraction pervading the lowest layers of the atmosphere in gaseous, liquid, and solid states.

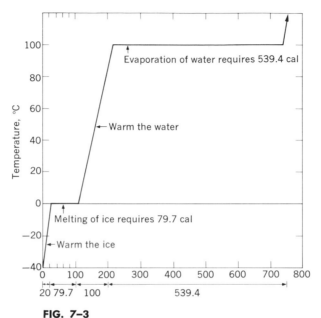

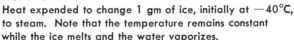

FIG. 7–3

Heat expended to change 1 gm of ice, initially at —40°C, to steam. Note that the temperature remains constant while the ice melts and the water vaporizes.

Heat Properties

Having established the basic structure of water, we are now prepared to understand why water plays such an important role in the heat balance of the earth. It has been calculated that to break all four hydrogen bonds in a mole (18 grams) of water, 6000 calories of heat energy would have to be expended. We recall that the calorie is defined as the amount of heat energy required to raise the temperature of one gram of water (a volume approximately the size of a sugar cube) one degree on the centigrade temperature scale. The tremendous heat expenditure required to change ice to steam is made more clear in graphical form, as in Fig. 7–3. It takes one-half calorie to raise the temperature of one gram of ice by one centigrade degree, and about 80 calories to melt it (the temperature remaining constant while the change of state occurs); 100 calories are required to raise the temperature of the water by 100 centigrade degrees; and 540 calories are required to change the water to a vapor at a temperature of 100°C. It should be emphasized that this is a fantastically large value compared to that for other liquids, and is a direct consequence of the strong hydrogen bonds which must be broken.

TABLE 7–2

Latent heat of vaporization

Substance	Temperature, °C	cal/g
Water	100.0	539.55
Water	0.0	595.9
Sulfuric acid	326.0	122.1
Sulfur dioxide	−10.0	94.9
Ammonia	0.0	301.6
Carbon dioxide	0.0	55.0
Hydrochloric acid	−84.3	98.7

Latent heat of fusion

Substance	Temperature, °C	cal/g
Water	0.0	79.7
Ice from sea water	−8.7	54.0
Carbon dioxide	−56.2	45.3
Ammonia	75.0	108.1
Wax (bee's)	61.8	42.3
Glycerol	18.0	47.5

TABLE 7–3

Specific heat

Substance	Temperature, °C	cal/g/C°
Water	15	1.0
Ice	−3	0.5
Ice	−40	0.43
Mercury	0	0.033
Aluminum oxide (Al_2O_3)	0	0.174
Silicon carbide	0	0.143
Calcium oxide (CaO)	0	0.177

The heats required to melt and vaporize one gram of the substance are referred to as the *latent heats of fusion* and *vaporization* respectively. Table 7–2 shows comparative values for other substances.

For heat capacity, other substances are compared to water as the standard. Thus, the *specific heat* (capacity) of water is designated as unity (i.e., one calorie/gram/centigrade degree or 1 cal/g/C°). Table 7–3 shows comparative values.

These considerations give the physical reasons for facts of nature which are a part of everyday common experience, such as the relative constancy of the temperature of a large body of water during a 24-hour span of sunlight and darkness, while the temperature of a nearby land surface changes from very hot during the midday to very cold in the hours before dawn. Because of the low heat capacity the temperature of the soil rises rapidly with the absorption of the solar radiation and drops rapidly because of the terrestrial infrared radiation.

Energy Bank

The vast oceans literally serve as an energy bank, taking in the vast deposits of solar energy and paying them out grudgingly to the atmosphere on demand. As there would be chaos in the financial world if all the banks paid out each night all the deposits made during the day, there would be climatological catastrophe of a dimension impossible to imagine, if the proportion of water surface to land surface were reversed and the earth's surface contained only a few small seas. If this were so, the major part of the earth's surface could well be one vast dust bowl, frigid at night, burning hot during the day, and scourged daily by winds of tornadic force.

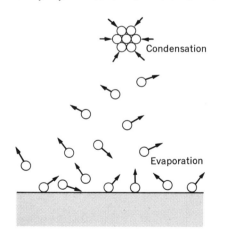

FIG. 7–4
Evaporation requires heat; condensation releases heat energy.

Fortunately this is not the case. Water molecules continually slip from the surface of bulk water sources into the atmosphere, each carrying an energy deposit of approximately 600 calories (since it requires more energy to change from a liquid to a gaseous state at, say, 20°C than at 100°C). These molecules of water are dispersed through the lower troposphere by vertical and horizontal air movements. When the circumstances are right, small groupings of individual molecules are again formed (that is, a water droplet is formed), and in this new location the energy deposits in the form of the latent heats of condensation are released to the atmosphere. See Fig. 7–4. What are these "right circumstances"? This brings us to the point where we must examine the details of the condensation process itself, this being a necessary preliminary to a discussion (in the next chapter) of the question of primary importance to the meteorologist and to the citizen: precipitation.

DESCRIPTION OF AIR

Constant Constituents

As we have seen, what we call "air" is a gas made up of different gases, some of which are plentiful and others very rare, continually mixed by atmospheric motions: 78.11 percent by volume is contributed by molecules of nitrogen; 20.95 percent by molecules of oxygen; 0.95 percent by argon; and trace percentages by other noble gases, hydrogen, and methane. In the lower layers of the atmosphere, i.e., the troposphere, these gases are always found in the same proportions.

Variable Constituents

Air contains a few other gases which are mavericks, so to speak, in the sense that they are present in variable amounts. Carbon dioxide (CO_2) comprises 0.01 to 0.1 percent, depending on the amount of combustion and photosynthesis and exchange with the ocean. Ozone, sulfur dioxide, and nitrogen dioxide are found in very small quantities. But by far the most important of the mavericks consists of molecules of H_2O. We call it water vapor. In equatorial maritime climates water vapor may be present in quantities ranging up to 7 percent of the atmosphere by volume. In other terms, one cubic yard might contain a tablespoon of water molecules. In arid desert regions, in the frigid Arctic, or at high elevations at the top of the troposphere (which ranges in summer from about 12 miles over the Tropics to 6 miles over the poles), water vapor is still present, but in negligible amounts. These gases make up our ocean of clean, pure air—a mixture which has evolved over a time span of millions of years.

The air found at the bottom of this atmospheric ocean is not clean. It is polluted by a variety of foreign matter which comes from both natural and man-made sources. The primary natural mechanism for introducing pollutants into the air is the frictional rubbing of the wind over the earth's surface. When this occurs over the land, surfaces of rocks are

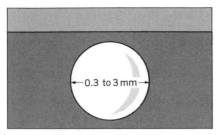

(a) Air bubble rises near surface.

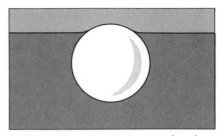

(b) Air bubble protrudes above surface forming cap which drains and thins.

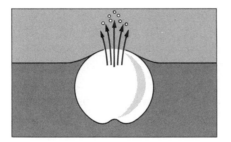

(c) Film cap ruptures. Air rushes out carrying film fragments which are now small droplets. Water fills cavity and initiates Rayleigh jet.

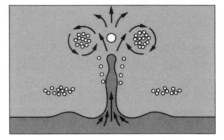

(d) Rayleigh jet rises and necks off forming drops which are thrown up at high speed. Note vortex ring of bubble-film droplets and lateral droplets.

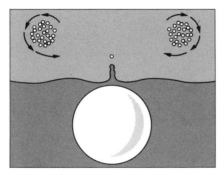

(e) After jet subsides a secondary jetlet is formed. Bubble film droplets now subside as new air bubble rises to surface.

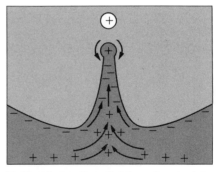

(f) Electrical action of jet as theorized by Blanchard. Jet drops carry positive charge brought from lower portion of the electrical double layer.

FIG. 7–5
Production of bubble film droplets.

slowly abraded, and further breakdown in particle size comes about by the polishing effect of small particles rolling over adjacent small particles, in somewhat the same way as agates are polished in a rock tumbler. The dust from this polishing effect is then fine enough to be carried aloft by the wind, and becomes more or less evenly distributed throughout the atmosphere. Dust storms, such as plagued the central states in the 1930's, are a dramatic example of this mechanism at work. A feature of considerable meteorological significance is that some of these particles are soluble in water (hygroscopic); others are wettable but not soluble; and still others are water-resistant (hydrophobic).

Frictional rubbing of wind over a water surface has the effect of generating waves. As the wind grows stronger, the amplitude or height of the wave increases (though there are other factors which must also be considered in determining the distance between adjacent wave tops). When the wind speed exceeds about 25 miles/hour, spray is pulled off the tops of the waves. Most of the spray droplets are so heavy they fall back into the water before evaporating. In the case of sea water, this mechanism may leave a tiny speck of salt from the smallest spray droplets which do evaporate, and this speck of salt is subsequently carried upward in the turbulent air.

A more effective mechanism for introducing salt particles into the air is the bursting of air bubbles found in the wake of unstable waves. Masses of water from the wave tops fall back into the ocean and carry air along with them. As this trapped air seeks release from the water, it rises in the form of bubbles of many sizes.

The sequence of events which occur as an air bubble reaches the surface and bursts is not only very fascinating to observe, but needs much study because of its meteorological significance. In Fig. 7–5 we see the several stages in the bursting of the air bubble. All bubbles greater in diameter than one millimeter (roughly, the size of a pinhead) depart from a spherical shape. However, at the water surface a film cap protrudes, which *is* spherical. Water drains down the sides of this cap until the film reaches a critical thinness, and then it ruptures. The burst happens with such speed that no researcher has yet satisfactorily recorded it even with high-speed cinephotography. The ligaments of the ruptured film snap together, becoming very small spherical droplets which are carried several millimeters into the air. Since they are so small, they rapidly evaporate and leave salt particles of the order of one-millionth of one-millionth (10^{-12}) of a gram, which are carried aloft by turbulence to higher elevations. Plate 7–1 shows one of the pictures of a bubble film burst taken by the author in the course of a recent study.

A secondary natural mechanism, which operates rather infrequently but sometimes with a massive effect, is that of volcanic eruption. When Mt. Krakatoa on the island of Java erupted in 1883, it produced an effect which was noticed in the upper atmosphere of the entire Northern Hemisphere for several years. Another secondary mechanism is injection of meteoric dust into the upper atmosphere as the earth moves in its orbit through dirty regions in space.

A further natural mechanism which produces small foreign particles is the reaction of the various trace gases and water vapor under the influence of solar radiation.

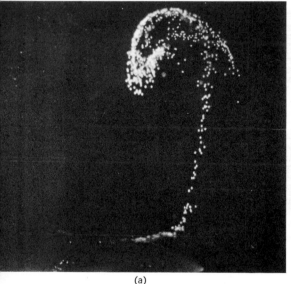

(a)

(b)

PLATE 7–1
Bursting air bubbles produce a pattern of bubble film droplets: (a) inverted-bowl effect shown by 3–400 bubble film droplets; (b) time exposure showing path of sinking bubble film droplets. Fall height is about 15 mm.

Combustion by-products pollute the atmosphere. Sometimes fires are set by purely natural causes, such as lightning strikes in dry forest areas. More frequently man strikes the fires to keep himself warm, to run his factories, to propel his automobiles, and so on. The by-products of combustion are ash, soot, tar, oils, hydrocarbons, sulfates, and sulfuric acid (where the fuel involves sulfur).

Today we have attained a reasonable understanding of the various kinds of air pollutants, particularly in the larger size range. In addition to knowing what they are and how they are produced, we know their size range and the range of concentration in which they are found. Perhaps most important of all, we are coming to understand the role they play with respect to the condensed water found in the atmosphere.

CLASSICAL DISCOVERIES

Cloud-Chamber Experiments

We would probably not know nearly so much as we do today were it not for a device called the cloud chamber. The first simple expansion cloud chamber was made in 1875 by Coulier in France in order to demonstrate that small foreign particles served as centers on which condensation took place. Air and water were enclosed in a flask. The air was super-saturated by compressing a hollow rubber ball connected to the flask. After the heat of compression was conducted away, Coulier suddenly released the ball to allow an expansion of the air and noted that a cloud of fine droplets was produced. Shortly thereafter (1880–1881) the Englishman J. Aitken, using similar but improved apparatus, showed that the cloud of fine droplets could be made more dense by introducing products of combustion, and that it could be thinned by one of several procedures: by filtering the air introduced into the cloud chamber through cotton wool, by allowing it to stand for several days before being used, or by allowing it to go through repeated cycles of cloud formation in the chamber. In the years following, Aitken developed various forms of an apparatus which became known as the Aitken dust counter. With it he undertook a complete survey of the small foreign particles, or nuclei, in the atmosphere. He also showed that the thickness (more accurately, the number of particles in a unit volume) of the cloud depended on how much the air in the chamber was expanded. After the most careful precautions were taken to remove all the foreign particles from the air, he found it was possible to produce a cloud of water droplets with a very large expansion. He was not sure, however, that he had been able to remove all the very small particles.

This problem was soon solved by another Englishman, C. T. R. Wilson, who in 1895 began his famous cloud-chamber experiments in the Cavendish Laboratory of Cambridge University, England. In Wilson's small glass cloud chamber, a given volume of air was subjected to a sudden expansion of a known amount. Excluding all known nuclei, he found that no visible effect was produced until the expansion ratio (the volume

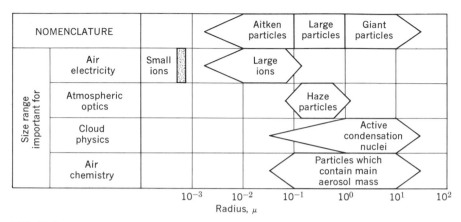

FIG. 7–6
Nomenclature of natural aerosols for various fields of meteorology. After C. E. Junge in *Advances in Geophysics*, ed. H. E. Landsberg, *et al.*, vol. 4, New York: Academic Press, 1958, p. 4, by permission.

after expansion compared to the volume before) reached a value of about 1.25, corresponding to a saturation ratio of 4 to 1. Then, with larger expansion, about a hundred drops per cubic centimeter (roughly, the volume of a small sugar cube) were always produced, regardless of attempts to filter them out. In February 1896, Wilson used the newly discovered x-rays to irradiate the filtered air put into the chamber. This time, at the same expansion ratio of 1.25, a much denser cloud was produced. This suggested that the nuclei on which the droplets formed were small ions, or charged particles. Some fifteen years then elapsed before Wilson succeeded in photographing these ions in the positions they occupied at the instant they were created, thus producing ion "tracks." (We might mention parenthetically that this was a real break-through point in nuclear physics, for it is this same Wilson cloud chamber which has been of such immense utility in identifying the tracks of the several kinds of nuclear particles, i.e., alpha and beta particles, the positron, and so on.) Increasing the expansion ratio beyond 1.38, corresponding to a saturation ratio of about 8 or a supersaturation of 700 percent, Wilson found he produced a cloud of very small droplets, distinct from the smaller number of larger droplets formed on the atmospheric ions. Later theoretical work formulated by Becker and Doring (1935) bolstered the idea that these droplets were produced on small groupings of water molecules, brought together momentarily by chance collisions in the highly supersaturated atmosphere of the cloud chamber.

As a result of the pioneer work of Coulier, Aitken, and Wilson, as well as subsequent investigations made by leaders in this field of research (Nolan and Pollak in Ireland, Mason in England, Findeisen and Schulz in Germany, D'Albe and Dessens in France, Woodcock and Blanchard in the U.S.A., and, of course, many others), there is general agreement that (a) the suspended solid and liquid particles (aerosols) vary in effect; (b) it is convenient to classify these particles according to differences in technique of observation—thus, the Aitken nuclei can be collected by electrostatic precipitators, by filters, and by coated slides, and giant nuclei can be collected on coated slides, detected by burning in a hydrogen flame, or analyzed in an electromicroscope—and (c) the range of concentration of foreign particles is immense, ranging from less than a few tens per cubic centimeter in mid-ocean to more than a million per cubic centimeter in the air of an industrial city on a smoggy day (see Fig. 7–6).

Up to this point we have confined our remarks to laboratory clouds formed in an expansion chamber. Let us now look to the larger laboratory of the atmosphere and see how clouds are formed in real situations.

CHAPTER 8

**Water
and
Ice
in
Clouds**

*Air is brought to a condition of saturation
primarily by cooling: cooling by contact, by
mixing, and by expansion, of which the last is by
far the most important. Orographic lifting,
ascent over frontal surfaces of air masses,
air-stream convergence, and local convection
are the four principal mechanisms which operate
in the atmosphere. We take another look at
the term* saturation, *defining it physically in
terms of molecules passing in equal numbers
across a plane liquid-gas (or solid-gas) interface.
Droplet growth rates are controlled by a compromise between the effect of droplet curvature
and the effect due to the hygroscopic nature
of the droplet nucleus. The characteristics of
ice are presented, and the basic hexagonal
shape is shown to be related to the particular
bonding directions associated with water molecules. After describing the various ice-crystal
shapes, we show how the ice-crystal habit is
related to temperature.*

WATER DROPLETS

Saturation

In previous chapters we established the fact that the amount of water vapor the air can hold is determined physically by the temperature and practically by the kind and number of cloud nuclei present. The condensation event may then be initiated either by decreasing the temperature of the air until excess water vapor over that permitted is "squeezed out," or by adding additional supplies of water vapor to the air at a given temperature until saturation is reached and the excess is again "squeezed out." (Sometimes both take place jointly.) The former method so greatly predominates over the latter that we give the latter only this nod of recognition, and concentrate on the basic methods of cooling, which are three in number.

Cooling by Contact

Air which moves or lies over a surface whose temperature is colder will be cooled by contact (i.e., by conduction). It is possible to bring such air eventually to saturation and produce the stratus-type cloud which we have defined as *fog* because it lies on the ground (or water).

Cooling by Mixing

Moist air which mixes with another colder air stream may be cooled to its saturation temperature, with the resultant production of a cloud form of water droplets or ice crystals, depending on the temperatures.

Cooling by Ascent

But by far the most important method of cooling is ascent. Air which rises experiences lower atmospheric pressure, and expands to occupy a greater volume. Since the work of expansion is done by the thermal energy of the air, the result of expansion is cooling. The cooling proceeds at a rate approximating 1 C° for each 100 meters of rise. This is the so-called dry adiabatic rate, which holds prior to condensation. (After condensation it decreases because of the counteracting effect of the released latent heat of condensation.) It can be seen that the rate of cooling depends on the rate of ascent, vertical motion providing the means of most rapid cooling. Whatever the case, it is much less than the cooling rates experienced in the cloud chambers described in the last chapter.

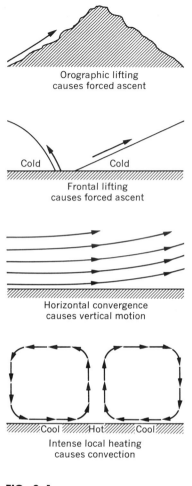

Orographic lifting
causes forced ascent

Cold   Cold

Frontal lifting
causes forced ascent

Horizontal convergence
causes vertical motion

Cool   Hot   Cool

Intense local heating
causes convection

FIG. 8–1

Four causes of air ascent.

There are several mechanisms for causing the air to rise and expand. The simplest and most obvious is called *orographic lifting.* The air finds some physical barrier, such as a range of hills, in its way and must flow up and over it. Sometimes the air itself provides such a barrier. Air which has its origin in the cold arctic or antarctic regions becomes very dense and heavy and hugs the lowest levels. Occasionally there are outbreaks of this cold dense air into lower latitudes, and the leading edge of the cold air (*the cold front*) acts like a snow plow, forcing aloft any warmer, lighter air which might lie in its path. Or, if the cold dense air has spent its equatorward thrust and is quiescent, warmer and lighter air sometimes glides slowly up over the gently sloping western side of the cold-air dome (i.e., up the *warm frontal* surface). At still other times horizontal squeezing, or *convergence,* of the air in the lower levels of an air stream causes a gentle ascent throughout a large volume of air. And occasionally air is locally warmed in its bottom layers by contact with the heated earth, and ascends vertically in a convective cell because of the buoyant forces acting on it. These several cases are shown diagrammatically in Fig. 8–1.

We have used the terms "saturation" and "supersaturation" rather frequently and perhaps too glibly in the preceding pages. Because it is very important that these terms be understood, we present a somewhat more detailed explanation of their meaning. Saturation is the physical condition at a gas-liquid or solid-liquid interface at which water vapor molecules leave and enter the liquid or solid surface at the same rate. It is important to emphasize that this definition refers to a flat (plane) surface.

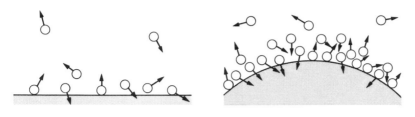

FIG. 8–2
At saturation molecules leave and enter the surface
at the same rate. Saturation vapor pressure is
greater over a curved than a plane surface.

Lakes and other large bodies of water are substantially flat surfaces. However, the surfaces of raindrops and small cloud droplets depart very markedly from flatness. The presence of a curved liquid surface enhances the ability of water molecules to escape across the liquid-gas interface. Equilibrium can be reestablished by having a condition of supersaturation present in the space surrounding the liquid. This effect is shown in Fig. 8–2. For instance, as the radius of the drop decreases to 0.5 micron, the humidity required to preserve equilibrium rises very rapidly. Yet as the radius becomes greater than 3 microns, equilibrium conditions approach those over a plane water surface.

Hygroscopic Nuclei

There is another effect which is relevant at this point. We remind the reader of the common experience of the clogging saltcellar on warm, humid days. This effect results from the fact that certain substances are "water-loving" or *hygroscopic*. Salt is a hygroscopic material. If we were to introduce a salt nucleus of a few tenths of a micron into moist air, it would start to grow at relative humidities as low as 85 percent. This is equivalent to saying that condensation has started, or that more water molecules are arriving than leaving. As the droplet grows, the salt solution weakens and the humidity required for equilibrium becomes greater. When the droplet has a radius of about 2 microns, it is so dilute that it can be considered as approximating pure water.

Nucleation Theory

The growth rate of a droplet is determined by the size and nature of the nucleus (i.e., whether or not there will be a solute effect), the supersaturation of the air, the rate of molecular movement of water vapor to the droplet, and the conduction of heat away from the droplet. This

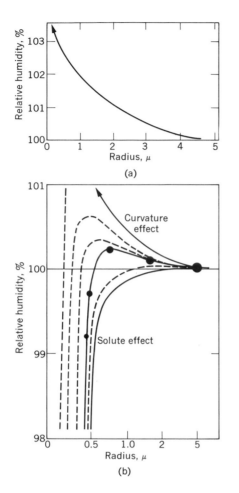

FIG. 8–3

(a) The value of relative humidity necessary for equilibrium increases rapidly as the droplet radius decreases below 1 micron. (b) The droplet growth rate is a compromise between curvature effect and the effect due to the hygroscopic nature of the nucleus (solute effect). The growth of droplet D is shown schematically at five stages of development. Smaller droplets require greater supersaturations to start their growth pattern.

means that a particular drop will initially have to experience a humidity which is high enough for it to grow larger than a certain critical size. Once it is past this barrier, normal growth can take place. This is shown in Fig. 8–3 in a series of curves A, B, C, D, and E for droplets of indicated starting sizes, E being greater than A. In the real atmosphere we observe that before the humidity reaches 100 percent, condensation starts on the larger hygroscopic nuclei. These grow rapidly to full-sized cloud droplets. As the humidity rises closer to 100 percent, more of the smaller nuclei are activated. As we have said, real atmospheric processes rarely yield supersaturations greater than a few tenths of one percent, quite in contrast with a laboratory cloud chamber in which supersaturations of several hundred percent can be reached. Consequently, only a fraction of the total foreign particles in the air, particularly in the smaller size range, ever become activated. Those which can become activated at low supersaturations are called *cloud nuclei*.

If these nuclei are indeed the building blocks of clouds, then variations in the kinds and amounts of nuclei should be reflected in the size and concentrations of droplets in clouds. This has been shown from work by Wieland, Squires, and Twomey in the early 1950's. Continental clouds can have as many as 1000 droplets/cubic centimeter, but their diameters are likely to average only 5 to 10 microns. Maritime clouds can have as few as 10 droplets/cubic centimeter, but of these many will have diameters as great as 50 microns. Since the minimum size of a raindrop capable of falling out of a cloud is of the order of one-tenth of one centimeter (1000 microns) or slightly less, a million or more continental cloud droplets are required to make up a raindrop's volume; but something less than 10,000 of the larger-sized maritime droplets are required. The job of coalescing raindrops is thus far more difficult in continental clouds than in maritime clouds; and, as many an inland farmer has noted when a "dry thunderstorm" has given a promise, and only a promise, of a welcome shower in time of drought, the process often fails entirely. The major cause of the difference in cloud microstructure appears to be the presence of far "thicker" concentrations of cloud nuclei over land than over water, all competing with each other for the available moisture.

ICE CRYSTALS

Supercooling

A particle of ice comes into being either through the freezing of a tiny droplet of water or by deposition directly from the vapor. It is an interesting fact that pure-water ice never melts until the temperature is raised to 0°C (disregarding changes due to pressure variations), but pure water quite frequently does not freeze when the temperature is lowered *below* 0°C. In fact, supercooled water is a common occurrence in the atmosphere when the water is present in small volumes, as in cloud droplets, even though bulk water nearly always starts to freeze at 0°C. However, there is a limit. It is impossible to supercool small droplets of absolutely pure water more than −40°C (which is also −40°F). This limit is based on many experiments. To understand this lower limit we need to think back to the structure of water, discussed in Chapter 7. As the temperature drops the thermal energy of the molecules decreases, and it becomes easier to establish all four of the hydrogen bonds which may be set up for each molecule. One can visualize small aggregates or colonies of molecules forming and breaking up within the larger mass. According to nucleation theory, one of these aggregates has to grow to a certain critical size in order to start the freezing process of pure water. When it passes this barrier it will then proceed to grow rapidly, and the remainder of the liquid will solidify. At −40°C it becomes statistically certain that an aggregate of this critical size will be reached, and rapidly. At higher temperatures an aggregate of the critical size *may* be reached. As the temperature approaches 0°C, the chance becomes less and less that it will be reached. This is a function of the relative strengths of the hydrogen bond and the disruptive motions due to thermal activity.

Characteristic Shape

The characteristic shape of ice is that of a six-sided geometrical figure called a *hexagon*. If one could visualize one water molecule bonded to four others, these four molecules would be found at the corner points of an imaginary tetrahedron (or four-sided figure made up of four isosceles triangles).

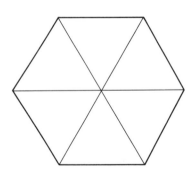

Seven molecules might well join up in an arrangement which would have the geometrical shape of two tetrahedra joined at the base. Fourteen molecules might then arrange themselves as six tetrahedra forming a hexagon. See Fig. 8–4, where this development is shown.

FIG. 8–4
The bases of six tetrahedra join to make a hexagon, the basic pattern of ice.

It is most instructive and satisfying for the reader to use toothpicks and glue and go through the construction of such a hexagonal shape for himself. The three-dimensionality of the figures sometimes does not come through clearly from the printed page to one not used to thinking in these terms. One word of warning, however: The boundaries of the tetrahedra do *not* represent the bonding directions, although a more accurate model, in which the bonding directions are shown, may be made with toothpicks and styrofoam balls. (See Fig. 8–5 for a more accurate picture of ice.) The simple exercise suggested gives only the hexagonality of the six tetrahedra.

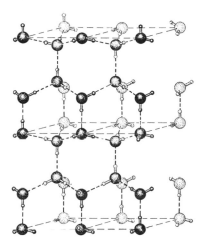

FIG. 8–5
Ice-crystal lattice (schematic); each oxygen atom is surrounded tetrahedrally at 2.76 A spacing (1 A $= 10^{-8}$ cm, $10^{-4}\,\mu$). Hydrogen protons lie 0.95 A from oxygen nuclei. From L. Pauling, *The Nature of the Chemical Bond*, Ithaca, N.Y.: Cornell University Press, 1960, p. 465, by permission.

Kinds of Crystals

Studies of ice-crystal forms found in nature show that a variety of shapes is possible. These are summarized in Fig. 8–6. Different arrangements are referred to by special terms (dendrites, flat plates, columns, cups, prismatic columns, hexagonal columns, needles, and hexagonal plates), but all are variations of the hexagonal shape.

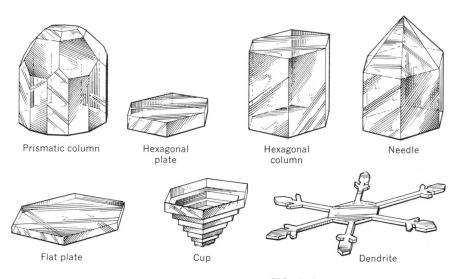

Prismatic column   Hexagonal plate   Hexagonal column   Needle

Flat plate   Cup   Dendrite

FIG. 8–6
Ice-crystal forms.

(a) Plates growing on the ends of needles

1mm

(b) Fern-shaped dendrites at −14°C

(c) Hollow prisms at −8°C
Courtesy B. J. Mason,
Imperial College, London.

PLATE 8–1
Ice crystals grown in a diffusion cloud chamber.

Once the ice particle starts to grow, what determines its future course of development? As the growth of a human personality depends on heredity (gene structure) and environment (home, school, community, etc.), so the embryo ice crystal is controlled by its "gene structure" (the hydrogen bonding of directions of H_2O which take on 105-degree angular separations from each other) and environment.

Ice Habit

Only recently have the relative effects of temperature and humidity been convincingly settled through research carried on by a group headed by B. J. Mason of Imperial College, London. Surprisingly, the *temperature* of the environmental air dictates the *form* of crystal; the *moisture* available controls the *rate of growth*. In Mason's experiments, crystals grown on a fiber in a cold box in which the temperature along the length of the fiber ranged from 0°C to −50°C and in which the humidity was varied, experiment to experiment, from minimal to 300 percent super-saturation, yielded the following results, summarized from many trials (refer to Plate 8–1):

Temperature, °C	Ice habit
0 to −3	Thin hexagonal plates
−3 to −5	Needles
−5 to −8	Hollow prismatic columns
−8 to −12	Hexagonal plates
−12 to −16	Dendritic, fernlike crystals
−16 to −25	Hexagonal plates
−25 to −50	Hollow prisms

These results correspond with observations of predominant ice-crystal forms in different atmospheric clouds.

Having spent one chapter describing the physical characteristics of water and the kinds of contamination found in the atmosphere, and a second describing the conditions which govern the growth of water droplets and ice crystals, we are now prepared to consider the all-important question of precipitation.

CHAPTER 9

**Precipitation:
Water
and
Ice
from
Clouds**

Precipitation is the "top rung" of the "ladder" of previous conditions and events discussed in the preceding two chapters. We start by defining the various kinds of precipitation hydrometeors. Then we list typical values of various size classes of drops. Growth of precipitation elements in a cloud environment at temperatures below freezing are seen to depend on the fact that there is a greater saturation vapor pressure over water than over ice at the same temperature. The Bergeron theory of precipitation derives from this. Precipitation which falls from warm (non-freezing) clouds is explained by means of the coalescence theory, details of which are presented. The chapter concludes with a summary of the total precipitation mechanism.

Why does rain fall from one cloud and not from another? What factors control the intensity of precipitation? Is there any scientific basis for man's hope to be able some day to make precipitation fall where and when he needs it, and in the proper quantities? Some partial answers to questions such as these have been acquired through research in cloud physics and atmospheric physical chemistry. Though present knowledge is anything but complete, there is enough understanding of the precipitation process to sketch in the broad outlines and some of the details. This is the task to which we turn in this chapter.

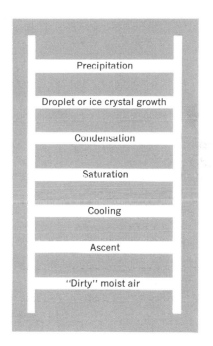

Precipitation is at the top of a "ladder" of preliminary events which lead up to it, as shown in Fig. 9–1. In previous chapters we have been climbing the rungs, one by one, starting with moist air and dynamic factors which bring about rising and cooling air.

The scope of the subject can be defined by a very simple statement. Tiny cloud droplets which are so light they remain substantially suspended in the air must somehow be caused to grow to a size, and thus a weight, which enables them to fall from the cloud and reach the earth before they evaporate. The *growth process* thus becomes the focus of a great part of cloud-physics research, and will be the principal concern of this chapter.

FIG. 9–1
"Precipitation ladder" showing the main steps leading to rain or snow.

DESCRIPTION OF HYDROMETEORS

By Definition

The precipitation problem can be approached in different ways: for example, in terms of descriptive categories. There are several different kinds of precipitation, called *hydrometeors,* which are distinctive enough to be given separate names. We list the official definitions taken from the 1956 *International Cloud Atlas* prepared by the World Meteorological Organization.

(1) **Rain.** *Precipitation of liquid water particles, either in the form of drops of more than 0.5-millimeter (0.02-inch) diameter or of smaller, widely scattered drops.*

Raindrops are normally larger than drops of drizzle. Nevertheless, drops falling on the edge of a rain zone may be as small as drizzle drops, because of partial evaporation; rain is then distinguished from drizzle by the fact that the drops are scattered. In certain cases, clouds may contain an abnormally large number of fine particles of dust or sand lifted from the ground in duststorms or sandstorms. These particles may fall to the ground with the raindrops (mud rain), often after being carried over great distances.

Freezing rain. *Rain, the drops of which freeze on impact with the ground, or with objects on the earth's surface, or with aircraft in flight.*

(2) **Drizzle.** *Fairly uniform precipitation composed exclusively of fine drops of water [diameter less than 0.5 millimeter (0.02 inch)], very close to one another.*

The drops appear almost to float, thus making even slight movements of the air visible.

Drizzle falls from a fairly continuous and dense layer of stratus, usually low, sometimes even touching the ground (fog). The amount of precipitation in the form of drizzle is sometimes considerable [up to 1 millimeter (0.04 inch) per hour], especially along coasts and in mountainous areas.

Freezing drizzle. *Drizzle, the drops of which freeze on impact with the ground, or with objects on the earth's surface, or with aircraft in flight.*

(3) **Snow.** *Precipitation of ice crystals, most of which are branched (sometimes star-shaped).*

The branched crystals are sometimes mixed with unbranched crystals. At temperatures higher than about −5°C (23°F), the crystals are generally agglomerated into snowflakes.

(4) **Snow pellets.** *Precipitation of white and opaque grains of ice. These grains are spherical or sometimes conical; their diameter is about 2–5 millimeters (0.1–0.2 inch).*

The grains are brittle and easily crushed; when they fall on hard ground, they bounce and often break up. Precipitation of snow pellets generally occurs in showers, together with precipitation of snowflakes or raindrops, when surface temperatures are about 0°C (32°F).

(5) *Snow grains. Precipitation of very small white and opaque grains of ice. These grains are fairly flat or elongated; their diameter is generally less than 1 millimeter (0.04 inch).*

When the grains hit hard ground, they do not bounce or shatter. They usually fall in very small quantities, mostly from stratus or from fog, and never in the form of a shower.

(6) *Ice pellets. Precipitation of transparent or translucent pellets of ice, which are spherical or irregular, rarely conical, and which have a diameter of 5 millimeters (0.2 inch) or less.*

The pellets of ice usually bounce when they hit hard ground, and make a sound on impact; they may be subdivided into two main types:

(a) frozen raindrops or largely melted and refrozen snowflakes (the freezing process usually takes place near the earth's surface);

(b) pellets of snow encased in a thin layer of ice which has formed from the freezing either of droplets intercepted by the pellets or of water resulting from the partial melting of the pellets.

(7) *Hail. Precipitation of small balls or pieces of ice (hailstones) with a diameter ranging from 5 to 50 millimeters (0.2 to 2.0 inches) or sometimes more, falling either separately or agglomerated into irregular lumps.*

Hailstones are composed almost exclusively of transparent ice, or of a series of transparent layers of ice, at least 1 millimeter (0.04 inch) in thickness, alternating with translucent layers. Hail falls are generally observed during heavy thunderstorms.

(8) *Ice prisms. A fall of unbranched ice crystals, in the form of needles, columns, or plates, often so tiny that they seem to be suspended in the air. These crystals may fall from a cloud or from a cloudless sky.*

The crystals are visible mainly when they glitter in the sunshine (diamond dust); they may then produce a luminous pillar or other halo phenomena. This hydrometeor, which is frequent in polar regions, occurs at very low temperatures and in stable air masses.

(9) *Fog. A suspension of very small water droplets in the air, generally reducing the horizontal visibility at the earth's surface to less than 1 kilometer (5/8 mile).*

When sufficiently illuminated, individual fog droplets are frequently visible to the naked eye; they are then often seen to be moving in a somewhat turbulent manner. The air in fog usually feels raw, clammy, or wet.

This hydrometeor forms a whitish veil which covers the landscape; when mixed with dust or smoke it may, however, take on a faint coloration, often yellowish. In the latter case, it is generally more persistent than when it consists of water droplets only.

Ice fog. A suspension of numerous minute ice crystals in the air, reducing the visibility at the earth's surface.

The crystals often glitter in the sunshine. Ice fog produces optical phenomena such as luminous pillars, small haloes, etc.

(10) **Mist.** *A suspension in the air of microscopic water droplets or wet hygroscopic particles, reducing the visibility at the earth's surface.*

The air in mist usually does not feel raw or clammy.

This hydrometeor generally forms a fairly thin, grayish veil which covers the landscape.

By Size, Concentration, etc.

Typical values of pertinent factors are summarized in Table 9–1.

TABLE 9–1.   Typical characteristics of various size classes of drops

Typical particle	Radius		Concen-tration	Terminal velocity, cm/sec	Volume relative to that of a cloud droplet
	microns	mm			
Cloud nucleus	0.1	0.0001	1000	0.0001	1/1,000,000
Cloud droplet	10.0	0.01	1000	1.0	1
Large cloud droplet	50.0	0.05	1	27.0	125/1
Borderline between cloud droplet and raindrop	100.0	0.1	–	70.0	1000/1
Drizzle drops	150.0	0.15	–	–	3375/1
Raindrop	1000.0	1.0	1	650.0	1,000,000/1
Heavy shower drops	3000.0	3.0	–	–	27,000,000/1

PRECIPITATION THEORIES

Another way to approach the precipitation problem is to take a look at the source of the precipitation, namely, the cloud mass, and analyze the way in which the cloud elements grow to fallout size.

In the previous chapter we were concerned with the growth of cloud droplets, and we saw that this was determined by the cloud-nucleus population (kind and concentration) and the "logistics" of water vapor (the amount on hand and the availability of replacement supplies).

It can be shown mathematically that if we start with a region at a temperature of 0°C, in which the supersaturation is kept at 0.05 percent, and introduce a salt nucleus of 0.1-micron radius, it requires 1 second to yield a water droplet of 1-micron radius, 10 minutes to yield a droplet of 8-micron radius, and 1 hour to yield a droplet of 20-micron radius. Subsequent growth by condensation becomes even slower. Even though this may be the primary mechanism for cloud production, it is completely inadequate as an explanation of how cloud droplets grow to hundreds of thousands of times their original volume in reasonably short periods of time, with the result that they can fall to the ground as raindrops.

The Wegener-Bergeron-Findeisen Theory

It so happens that the saturation vapor pressure over a plane (flat) ice surface is less than that over a plane water surface at the same temperature. Expressed in another way, saturation over water at −10°C represents 10 percent supersaturation over ice; saturation over water at −20°C represents 21 percent supersaturation over ice at that temperature. As early as 1911 it was pointed out by the German meteorologist Wegener that the effect of the coexistence of ice and supercooled water would be that the vapor pressure in such a region would take on an intermediate value, and he predicted:

> "the effect of this must then be, that condensation will take place continually on the ice, whereas at the same time the liquid water evaporates (from the droplets), and this process must go on until the liquid phase is entirely consumed."

This process can be seen schematically in Fig. 9–2.

An important contribution was made in the 1930's by the great Swedish meteorologist Tor Bergeron through his classic paper "On the Physics of Clouds and Precipitation." Bergeron incorporated Wegener's idea into a theory which suggested that every raindrop of radius greater than 250 microns has its origin as a particle of ice. The implication of this theory was that the tops of all rain clouds must extend above the 0°C isotherm.

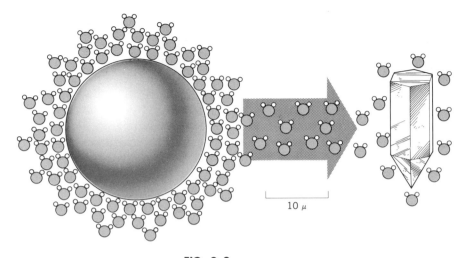

FIG. 9–2
Greater saturation vapor pressure over water surface
than over ice surface causes supercooled droplets
to evaporate and ice crystals to grow.

We can appreciate what may take place in the top of a cloud which extends well above the freezing level. Let us assume that its temperature is as low as −15°C, and that the cloud top contains both ice crystals and supercooled waterdrops. As Wegener said, the vapor-pressure gradient will be such as to cause the waterdrops to evaporate and the ice crystals to grow. But at this temperature the preferred growth habit will be that of dendrites, i.e., fernlike sprouting which takes place preferentially at the corners of the plates. As this continues a snowflake is formed, which may grow heavy enough to start to fall from the cloud. As it does its arms entwine with the arms of others. Then, depending on various other factors, principally the thickness of the cloud and the height of the freezing level above the ground, the snowflake may reach the ground as snow, or it may melt *en route* and become a raindrop before it strikes the earth.

The implication of Bergeron's theory was that the tops of all rain clouds must extend above the 0°C isotherm. Additional important contributions were made in the late 1930's by the German meteorologist Findeisen, whose analysis of upper-air observations in northern Europe confirmed Bergeron's hypothesis. The Wegener-Bergeron-Findeisen theory held predominance for a decade or so as a description of the primary precipitation mechanism.

Then an accumulation of new information documented the fact that substantial quantities of rain did fall from warm clouds, clouds whose

tops definitely did not penetrate the freezing level. This forced meteorologists to focus their attention on other mechanisms of raindrop growth.
Of these the mechanism of accretion by coalescence seemed most likely
to explain the observed patterns.

Coalescence Theory

The very idea of collision suggests relative motion. There is no possibility of collision on a freeway when all cars are moving along at the
same speed and in parallel lines. In contrast, the most serious freeway
collisions occur when one car is forced to stop and, often in a dense fog
and with reduced visibility, other cars in the traffic line successively pile
into (coalesce with) the obstacle ahead.

Let us first consider the motion of spheres of water relative to still
air. We recall that an object will be accelerated until all the forces
acting on it are balanced, and then it will move with constant speed.
A sphere of water in still air will be acted on by three forces: (1) gravity,
(2) buoyancy of the air, (3) the frictional retarding force. The frictional
force is proportional to the velocity. When the sphere falls at a speed
such that the drag is equal to the difference between the force of gravity
and the buoyant force, it has reached its *terminal velocity*, as seen in
Fig. 9–3.

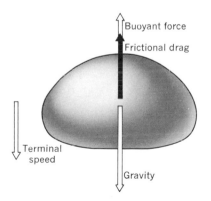

FIG. 9–3
Drop falling at terminal speed. Its spherical
shape becomes distorted.

Table 9–2 shows that the terminal velocity for small spheres is very
low. Therefore, it does not take much updraft in a cloud to keep cloud
droplets suspended at the same level. The terminal velocity for raindrops (which, incidentally, change from spherical shape to that of round
loaves of bread with flat bottoms) is quite high in comparison.

TABLE 9–2   Terminal velocity of raindrops and cloud droplets in still air

Diameter, microns	Rate of fall		Type of drop
	ft/min	m/sec	
5000	1750	8.9	Large raindrop
1000	790	4.0	Small raindrop
500	555	2.8	Fine rain or large drizzle
200	300	1.5	Drizzle
100	59	0.3	Large cloud droplet
50	15	0.076 ⎱	Ordinary cloud droplet
10	0.6	0.003 ⎰	
2	0.023	0.00012 ⎱	Incipient drops and nuclei
1	0.007	0.00004 ⎰	

The German meteorologist Findeisen worked out another interesting set of figures, namely, the fall distance of drops in an atmosphere of 90 percent relative humidity (RH) before evaporation (Table 9–3). The point to be noted is the small distance that cloud droplets fall before evaporation. This emphasizes again the point that a cloud must be considered as a dynamic system in which both evaporation and condensation are going on continuously.

Assume now, for the moment, a cloud in which there is a droplet-size variation of a factor of 100, say from 10-micron radii to 1000-micron radii, and all the droplets are falling through still air at their terminal velocity. An observer on the 1000-micron drop would see the 10-micron droplets moving upward at 789.4 feet/minute. But what happens to those 10-micron droplets which happen to lie "in the way" of the large drop, i.e., lie within the cylinder of space being swept by the large drop?

TABLE 9–3
Distance of fall before evaporation (after Findeisen)

RH = 90%,   p = 900 mb,   t = 5°C

Radius of drop, microns	Distance of fall	Type of drop
1	3.3×10^{-4} cm	Cloud droplets
10	3.3 cm	
100	150 m	Raindrops
1000	42 km	
2500	280 km	

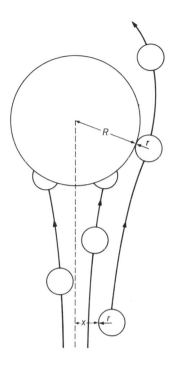

Air moves around the falling large drop in a more or less regular streamline pattern. The majority of the small droplets will follow this streamline pattern and thus avoid collision. Figure 9–4 shows one droplet which originally lay a distance of *x* from the center line of the large drop, yet, following the streamlines, just grazed the edge of the large drop as it went by. If we designate the radius of the droplet by *r* and the radius of the large drop by *R*, we can define a *collision efficiency E* by the ratio of the cross-section area of two cylinders:

$$E = \frac{\pi x^2}{\pi (R + r)^2}$$

or

$$E = \frac{x^2}{(R + r)^2} .$$

FIG. 9–4
Streamline flow around larger drop. Small drops must be closer than x to the center line if they are to make contact with larger drops.

This efficiency has a maximum possible value of unity, which would mean that the large drop captures every droplet in its fall path. This is never the case. The actual value of *E* depends on the sizes and relative fall velocities of the drop and the droplets, and on the density and viscosity of the air. In the case of the 10-micron droplet and 1000-micron drop, the mathematics of the airflow works out relatively simply and *E* can be computed. It turns out to be zero. When the ratio of the radius of the droplet to that of the drop is less than 0.2, all the small droplets follow the streamlines around the large drop. The mathematical problem becomes much more complicated when the drops are more nearly the same size, for here the airflow patterns of one interfere with those of the other. The highest collision efficiencies seem to occur when the ratio of radii is between 0.6 and 0.7. When the droplet is large and the drop small, i.e., when the ratio increases above 0.9, the collision efficiency again drops rapidly to zero. This is the case for drops of nearly equal size.

When a droplet and a drop do collide, they either coalesce or bounce apart. If drops of nearly the same size collide at high velocity they may coalesce temporarily while they oscillate violently and then break up again in smaller fragments. Whether or not a droplet will bounce as it hits a large drop depends on the size of the droplet, its velocity, and the impact angle.

We can now define a *coalescence efficiency* as the ratio of the number of droplets which coalesce with the large drop to those which collide with it. A third efficiency, the *accretion efficiency*, is then the product of the collision efficiency and the coalescence efficiency and tells us, in principle, what we want to know: the *drop growth rate*.

Cloud physicists are much concerned with the problem of evaluating the coalescence efficiency as a step toward the accretion efficiency. Unfortunately, it is very difficult to evaluate, for it depends on a variety of factors such as the strength of the electric field prevailing at the time, the angle of impact of the small on the large drop, and the relative sizes of the drops, to mention a few.

We find that droplets grow, up to a radius of about 20 microns, primarily by the process of condensation, after which coalescence becomes important, if other conditions are favorable. The principal "other" condition is a cloud in which there is a range or spectrum of droplet sizes which yields the relative velocities necessary for collision and coalescence. This condition can be traced back to the spectrum of cloud nuclei (number and kind) which become activated. This in turn depends on the dynamics of the flow patterns, such as the strengths of the large- and small-scale vertical currents, and the extent to which the air is loaded with moisture so that water supplies removed by condensation may be replenished and the saturation kept high.

In order to summarize the many details presented in this chapter, we use Mason's chart, shown as Fig. 9–5. Reading it from left to right, we see that in larger clouds which contain small vertical velocities, drizzle drops fall when coalescence builds up drops of a size which can fall from the cloud and reach the earth before they evaporate. When the cloud is above the freezing level, and the temperature is below freezing, dendritic crystals grow by accretion from the vapor or sublimation. Such ice crystals may fall as snow, or melt *en route* to the ground, depending on the vertical distribution of temperature. If the cold cloud is of the cumulus type with large vertical velocities, coagulation of the ice crystal with supercooled drops may develop *graupel*, which can melt and form a raindrop. Or the crystal may become a wet *hailstone*, which at a later time sheds its liquid coat to produce large drops. These drops may, in turn, enter into a chain reaction which will produce many raindrops. In

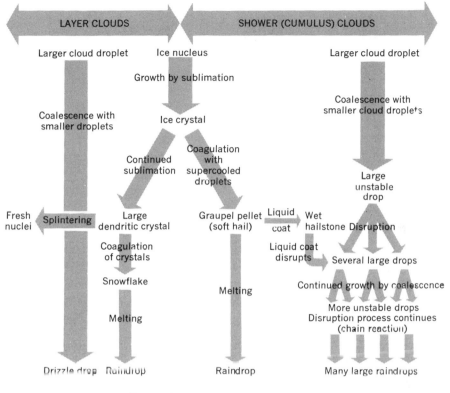

FIG. 9–5
A schematic diagram showing natural precipitation mechanisms.

the case of warm shower clouds, coalescence between smaller drops and a large drop may cause the large drop to grow to an unstable size, thus setting up conditions for the development of many large raindrops from the shattering of the unstable drop.

Although the last three chapters may leave the novice with the impression that we understand the precipitation process very well, this is not the case. Precipitation is an immensely complex subject and cloud physicists understand only the bare essentials. The whole purpose of cloud-physics research is to enlarge man's knowledge about this process which is so essential to the maintenance of life on this planet.

CHAPTER 10

**Atmospheric
Electricity**

*The earth-atmosphere-sun is considered as an
electric system. Basic electrical concepts are
defined: law of repulsion and attraction, electric
field, potential, current, resistance, and capacitance. These are then applied to the atmosphere.
We tell the scientific mystery story whose solution
showed how the electric charge lost from the
earth's surface was replaced by the activity of
thunderstorms. Then we examine the thunderstorm to see how it generates positive and
negative charge. This leads to a description of
Mason's ice-splintering mechanism. Presentation
of the details of the lightning stroke and the
production of thunder concludes the chapter.*

In the past several chapters we have been considering the sun-air-earth system as a vast thermodynamic machine in which solar fuel is used to accelerate the millions of tons of air making up the atmosphere and the billions of tons of water in the oceans, seas, and rivers. The resulting motion can be thought of as an immensely complex safety-value action through which surplus heat energy is moved from low to high latitudes. If, for some reason, the safety-valve mechanism were to cease to work, the result would be literally boiling tropical seas and bone-numbing arctic wastelands—a most unpleasant prospect.

The feel of the wind upon our faces reminds us of the motion which results from the heat imbalance. However, the sight of the lightning flash from a black thunderhead is a vivid reminder that the sun-air-earth system is also electric. In this chapter we will examine this electric system first in the broad context of electricity in general, then more specifically in terms of the role played by the thunderstorm. Before we can describe the electrical nature of the sun-air-earth system we must master the vocabulary of electricity, and to give this a bit of flavor we make a brief historical digression.

BASIC ELECTRICITY

Positive and Negative Charge

Benjamin Franklin (1706–1790), that tremendously versatile businessman-statesman-scientist, first recognized that there were two, and only two, kinds of electric charge to be found in nature. To these he affixed the names "positive" and "negative." Bodies carrying the same kinds of electricity were found to dislike each other; bodies carrying different kinds liked each other. From this came the basic law of static electricity: "Like charges repel, unlike charges attract." The French scientist Charles Augustin de Coulomb (1736–1806) found, in experimenting with point charges, that distance affected the magnitude of the force of attraction or repulsion. When the distance between the points was doubled, the force was found to decrease by a factor of four; when it was tripled, the force decreased by a factor of nine, and so on. In shorthand form, the Coulomb "inverse square" law of electrostatics is written $F = qq'/d^2$, where F is the force, q and q' are the magnitudes of the point charges, and d is the distance separating them.

When the physicist talks about the effect of one charge on another, he uses the concept of an *electric field* (of influence). He visualizes the concept of a positive test charge of unit strength at a certain point. The value of the electric field is measured by the direction and magnitude of

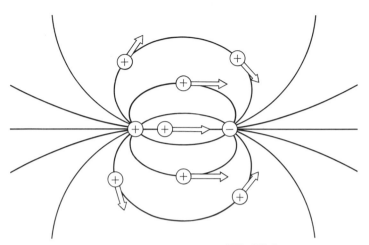

FIG. 10–1

Electric field in vicinity of positive and negative charge. The small circles represent small positive test charge. The spacing of the electric-field lines gives a measure of its force (close spacing means strong force).

the force exerted upon the test charge placed at the point in question, as seen in Fig. 10–1.

These discoveries were all made before the inner structure of the atom was understood. We now know that positively charged bodies simply contain more protons than electrons; negatively charged bodies contain more electrons than protons. Neutral bodies have the same number of protons and electrons. How, then, do bodies acquire a positive or negative charge? Evidently there must be a separation of charge.

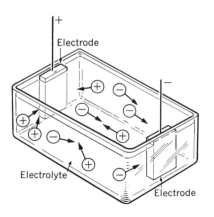

FIG. 10–2

Schematic separation of charge by storage-battery action. Negative ions deposit charge on the right-hand electrode, making it negative; positive ions neutralize themselves by taking electrons from the left-hand electrode, leaving it with positive charge.

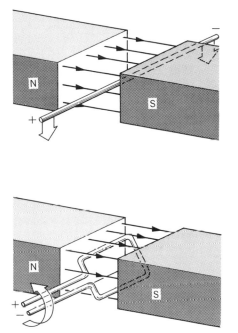

FIG. 10-3
A single wire caused to move through a magnetic field develops negative charge at one end, positive at the other. If the single wire is made into a loop, this device generates alternating current (ac) as it rotates.

Charge Separation

There are several charge-separating mechanisms. One of the most common is *chemical,* and is used in the common device we know as a battery. In this case a chemical reaction occurs between metallic electrodes and an electrolyte such that a positive charge builds up on one electrode and a negative on the other, as in Fig. 10–2. A second is *motional.* It was found in the early 19th century that the motion of a conductor perpendicular to a magnetic field creates a force, perpendicular to both the magnetic field and the direction of motion, which acts on the charges in the conductor. This is what takes place in the "generation of electricity" at a hydroelectric power station. The potential energy of water stored in a dam is used to move the conductors of an armature in a magnetic field. Figure 10–3 shows how the loosely bound electrons in a simple armature conductor are forced to one end of the conductor as a result of this motion, giving it a negative charge and leaving the other end with an electron deficit, i.e., a positive charge. When a transmission line is connnected to the output terminals of the generator, and is brought into one's house, the charge separation established at the generator enables one to light and heat the house and operate electrical appliances. (We have grossly oversimplified a complex system to make our point.)

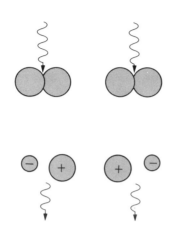

Sometimes charge is separated by *bombardment*. If a molecule absorbs certain radiation-light quanta, or is struck by a sufficiently energetic particle, it can be set into such a state of violent inner motion that it breaks apart into two charged fragments called ions, as in Fig. 10–4. This is what causes the molecular dissociation of the oxygen molecule in the high stratosphere on absorption of solar radiation.

FIG. 10–4
Molecules may break into two charged atoms (ions) when struck by radiation of proper frequency or by a high-energy particle.

Potential

In each of these three cases work is done to produce the charge separation. The ratio of the work done to the charge separated defines a very important electrical concept, the electric *potential* (more commonly referred to as potential difference), written as $V = W/q$, where V stands for potential, W stands for work done, and q stands for unit charge separated.

The like charges which have been driven to opposite electrodes of a battery, or to opposite terminals of a generator (dynamo), experience the mutual force of repulsion prescribed by the Coulomb law, and look for ways and means of moving elsewhere to relieve this force. This is somewhat analogous to the way population pressure makes people look around for lands to which they can emigrate. Just as these people must have transportation to cross the miles between the old and the new homeland, electric charges must find conducting paths if the "population pressure" of positive and negative charges is to be reduced.

Current

Certain materials found in nature, such as copper, silver, and tungsten, have an electron-shell structure which contains a loosely bound outer electron. These electrons tend to wander from atom to atom like tramps. When an electric potential is applied at the ends of a wire made of these materials the free electrons in it experience a force which pushes them toward the positive terminal—the region of electron deficit, as in Fig. 10–5. The rate at which the electrons move past an arbitrary check point

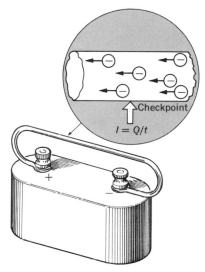

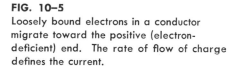

FIG. 10–5
Loosely bound electrons in a conductor
migrate toward the positive (electron-
deficient) end. The rate of flow of charge
defines the current.

defines the *current*, which is expressed analytically as $I = q/t$, in which
I is the current, q the charge, and t the time. If the sense of the potential
is constant, the charges move only in one direction, and we refer to this
as dc or direct current. If the potential changes periodically, the charges
in the conductor surge first one way and then the other, and we refer to
this as ac or alternating current. The electrical resistance to the dc flow
of charge can be stated as the ratio of the applied potential to the current,
$R = V/I$. This is the famous Ohm law of electricity, named after the
discoverer, Georg Simon Ohm (1787–1854).

Capacitance

Sometimes it is desirable to store up the charge which is separated by
the battery or generator. Under these circumstances the source of potential (called the electromotive force or emf) is connected electrically to a
device called a capacitor. In its simplest form it consists of two parallel
conducting plates, separated from each other by a nonconducting medium such as air. Work has to be done in storing charge on the plates of
a capacitor. When charged, each plate takes on an opposite charge. The
charge-storing ability of the capacitor, known as the *capacitance*, is defined as the ratio of charge stored to the potential established between
the plates, $C = Q/V$.

A capacitor can be overcharged. When this happens the electric field
between the plates becomes so great that the intervening medium, called
the dielectric, breaks down and becomes a conducting path. This is to

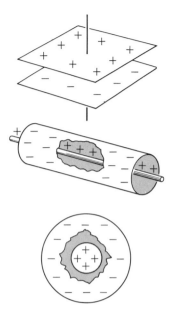

say that the positive and negative charges on the plates exert such a pull on the negative and positive (respectively) charges of the dielectric atoms that ionization is produced, the negative ions moving to the positive plate and the positive ions moving to the negative plate.

Capacitors take one of three basic geometrical shapes, as shown in Fig. 10–6. The simplest, as has been said, consists of two parallel plates. A cylindrical capacitor involves a central conductor (rod or wire) surrounded by a conducting sleeve. A coaxial cable is an example of this type of capacitor. A spherical capacitor consists of a spherical shell surrounding an interior conducting sphere.

FIG. 10–6
Three basic shapes of capacitors: (a) parallel plate, (b) cylindrical, (c) spherical.

Electrical Concepts

Before going ahead to this application, we summarize our newly acquired electrical vocabulary in Table 10–1. We have advanced step by step to the point where we can now apply these ideas to the earth and its atmosphere.

TABLE 10–1.   Summary of basic electrical concepts

Electrical concept	Definition	Unit, mks
Charge	(fundamental)	coulomb
Electric-field strength	$E = F/q$	$\dfrac{\text{volt}}{\text{meter}} = \dfrac{\text{newton}}{\text{coulomb}}$
Potential	$V = W/Q$	$\text{volt} = \dfrac{\text{joule}}{\text{coulomb}}$
Current	$I = Q/t$	$\text{ampere} = \dfrac{\text{coulomb}}{\text{second}}$
Capacitance	$C = Q/V$	$\text{farad} = \dfrac{\text{coulomb}}{\text{volt}}$
Ohm's law	$V = IR$	$\text{volt} = \text{ampere} \times \text{ohm}$
Coulomb's law	$F = \text{const} \cdot \dfrac{qq'}{d^2}$	$\text{newton} = \dfrac{\text{coulomb}^2}{m^2}$

APPLICATION TO ATMOSPHERE

The Earth as Capacitor

The earth, with its surplus of electrons, surrounded by the electron-hungry ionosphere, is an example of a charged spherical capacitor, as shown in Fig. 10–7. The charge carried by the earth has been determined to be about 400,000 coulombs (an extremely large value, since the coulomb is a very large unit of charge). As indicated in an earlier chapter, the ionosphere is to be found at a height of about 100 kilometers. Taking these values and the dielectric constant of the air, we compute the potential difference between the "plates" to be about 360,000 volts. This changes with height at sea level at a rate of about 100 volts/meter, and less rapidly at higher elevation. It is a bit startling to realize that the difference in the electric potential between one's head and feet is nearly 200 volts! (The reason we do not notice any effect is that the electrical resistance of our bodies is very high, thus limiting any currents to insignificantly small values.)

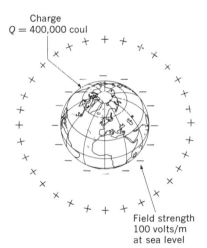

Charge
Q = 400,000 coul

Field strength
100 volts/m
at sea level

FIG. 10–7
The earth-conosphere comprises a vast spherical capacitor.

Maintenance of the Earth's Charge

These facts bring us to a fine scientific mystery story which had its origin nearly a hundred years ago, well before the existence of the ionosphere had been suspected. It had been known that in some way electric charge leaked off a charged body into the air, and that, other factors being equal, this took place most effectively from objects which had sharp points, such as corners of buildings, blades of grass, trees, etc. (The development of the lightning rod was a direct consequence of this knowledge.) The central mystery was how the earth could maintain its charge while it was continually losing it at the substantial rate of about 1800 coulombs/second, or 1800 amperes. A secondary aspect of the mystery was the means by which the charge moved from the earth to the air. This latter aspect was solved by the end of the 19th century through the discovery of ions in the atmosphere, which moved under the influence of the electric field measured at the earth's surface, positive ions being pulled earthward and negative ions being repelled upward. But how were these atmospheric ions produced? It so happened that the important discovery of radioactivity had been made just a few years earlier by Becquerel and the Curies. Two German physicists, Elster and Geitel, were the first to suggest that emanations from radioactive atoms in the earth's crust and in radon gas were the cause of the atmospheric ions, pairs of positive and negative ions being produced when neutral atoms were struck by the high-energy alpha or gamma rays. It seemed logical that ionization should be less at greater distances from the earth. The Austrian physicist Victor Hess decided to test this conclusion, and in 1911 he made an historic balloon flight to an altitude of 16,000 feet. Instead of confirming the idea that the ionization should decrease with altitude, his instruments indicated that it increased! Why? The only possible answer seemed to be that in some unknown way an ionizing agent from above (from the cosmos) penetrated the atmosphere. Thus emerged the concept of "cosmic rays." These energetic visitors are now rather well understood, but not completely. They have been found, in the main, to be high-energy protons shot earthward from the sun, though a small fraction presumably come from other, more distant suns. They enter the earth's atmosphere from all directions, collide with air molecules, and impart some of their energy to them. These energetic particles, called secondary cosmic rays, then proceed to collide with still other air molecules and ionize them.

The main mystery still remained. Granting the presence of ions produced by radioactive atoms and primary and secondary cosmic rays, how does the charge on the earth maintain its constant value?

Role of the Thunderstorm

The principal clue to the solution of this mystery was the behavior of the electric field in the vicinity of the earth, and the principal early sleuth was the British physicist C. T. R. Wilson, whom we encountered earlier. Wilson found that in fair weather the electric field was steady, and so directed that positive ions would be drawn downward. But in thundery weather the electric field tended to fluctuate wildly from low to very

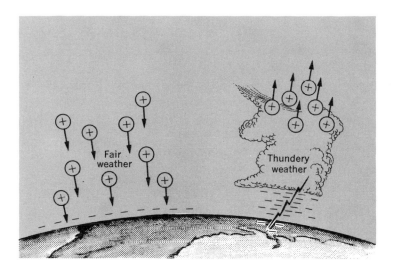

FIG. 10–8

In fair weather, heavy positive ions drift earthward and neutralize the earth's negative charge. In thundery weather the thunderstorm pours negative charge earthward to restore the loss.

high values. Sometimes it even reversed its direction. This suggested to Wilson that in fair weather the loss of charge from the earth was the result of its neutralization by the heavy positive ions which slowly drifted earthward, and that the thunderstorm, in a way only dimly understood, might be the agent which poured a replacement of the lost negative charge down to the earth during the periods of field reversal. See Fig. 10–8. This basic hypothesis, made in 1920, has withstood the test of nearly half a century of further investigation, and still stands as the basic mechanism.

One of the strongest bits of substantiating evidence has been found in studies made by the English meteorologist F. F. W. Whipple. He correlated the world-wide area covered by thunderstorms at different Greenwich hours over the land, with the average diurnal variation of sea-level electric-field intensity found over the ocean. As seen in Fig. 10–9, the correlation is surprisingly exact. Both curves reach a minimum at about 0400 GMT hours, and a maximum at about 2000 GMT hours. This becomes quite reasonable when one remembers that 2000 hours corresponds to midday in the Western Hemisphere and early evening over equatorial Africa, both times being favorable for thunderstorm activity.

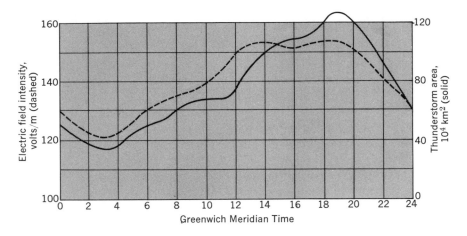

FIG. 10–9

Whipple's correlation of worldwide thunderstorm area (over land) and diurnal variation of electric field intensity (over oceans).

An investigation carried on by Gish and Wait in the early 1950's provided further confirmation of this line of reasoning. Feeling that it would be easier to fly over thunderstorms and measure the upward flow of positive charge to the higher atmosphere than to fly underneath in the turbulent air and try to measure the downward surge of negative charge, they conducted a series of research flights using high-flying B-29 aircraft, and found that the average value of upward flow of charge ranged from 0.3 to 0.6 ampere for each thunderstorm cell. Assuming that this equaled the downward flow of negative charge from the thunderstorm, and that the latter had to compensate for the 1800-ampere leakage current from the earth, this would necessitate 3000–6000 thunderstorm cells over the earth each day. Climatological data indicate that this is an entirely reasonable estimate.

The question now shifts. If the thunderstorm is the means by which the earth's negative charge is replenished, how does it accomplish the task?

THEORY OF THUNDERSTORM ELECTRIFICATION

Cloud physicists have been greatly concerned with this question which, in effect, asks for the development of an adequate theory of thunderstorm electrification. The basic theory must explain quantitatively (in numbers) how electric charge is generated and separated in a thundercloud at a rate equal to that at which it is dissipated in lightning flashes. It must be consistent with all the well-established facts accumulated in the years in which these storms have been studied.

Conditions

B. J. Mason of Imperial College has listed six basic sets of conditions which, in his judgment, such a theory must take into account. These are presented as a working hypothesis which has as yet to gain the full support of the majority of atmospheric scientists.

1. In a typical thunderstorm cell, charge is generated and separated in a volume bounded by the 0°C and −40°C levels, having a typical radius of 2 kilometers, and therefore a volume of about 50 cubic kilometers.

2. The negative charge is centered near the −5°C level, while the main positive charge is located several kilometers higher; a secondary positive charge often exists near the cloud base where the temperature is usually a little warmer than 0°C.

3. The average duration of precipitation and lightning from a single thunderstorm cell is about 30 minutes.

4. A typical cell produces lightning flashes at intervals of about 20 seconds; the average electric moment (value of charge times the separation of charge) is about 100 coulomb·kilometers, i.e., 20 coulombs times 5 kilometers. Therefore, the average lightning current is about 1 ampere.

5. The magnitude of the charge which is being separated immediately after a flash, by virtue of the speed of fall of the precipitation elements, is of the order of 1000 coulombs.

6. Sufficient charge must be generated and separated to supply the first lightning flash within 10–20 minutes of the first appearance of precipitation particles large enough to produce a radar echo.

In summary, the requirement is to generate about 1000 coulombs of charge in a volume of about 50 cubic kilometers in a period of about 20 minutes at an average rate of 1 coulomb/cubic kilometer/minute.

All evidence points toward the fact that precipitation is intimately related to the electrification process. Since the region of main charge separation lies above the 0°C isotherm level, it is logical to associate the generation of charge with the growth of ice particles.

Experimental Verification

Experiments have been carried on in Mason's laboratory to study the electrification of an artificial hailstone by the impaction, freezing, and splintering of supercooled droplets on its surface. These experiments showed that impacting droplets less than 30 microns in diameter produced very little electrification, and that very large drops which produced splashing over the face of the hailstone likewise produced no clear effect. But in the case of a typical droplet of 80 microns in diameter which moved through $-15°C$ air, struck the hailstone at a speed of 10 meters/ second, and froze, an average of 12 positively charged ice splinters were produced and a small negative charge (of 4×10^{-6} electrostatic unit, esu) was left on the hailstone.

Making reasonable assumptions about the concentration of hail pellets in a thunderstorm, the concentration of droplets greater than 30 microns in diameter, the rate of impaction, and the charge generated per impact, Mason concluded that this mechanism is capable of producing the electric charge and fields required by observation. Therefore, this is probably the main mechanism of thunderstorm electrification.

We need to examine the freezing mechanism more carefully to see why the ice splinters should be produced, and why they carry a positive charge. After impaction, and during the early stages of freezing, a shell of ice starts to form around the outside of the drop. The release of latent heat of fusion warms the remaining water in the droplet to $0°C$. This means that a temperature gradient exists in the droplet. The freezing of the liquid interior then proceeds at a rate determined by the speed with which the heat can be dissipated to the surroundings. It seems that the result of the temperature gradient in ice is thermal dissociation of some small fraction of the ice molecules. These ions tend to diffuse from the warm to the cold temperature. Since the protons (H^+) are ten times as mobile as the hydroxyl ions (OH^-), the former tend to build up at the outer surface of the drop, and there they produce a positive space charge. When the center core of water freezes the resulting expansion bursts the frozen outer shell. Splinters of positive ice are then ejected. When these break off they leave a negatively charged ice ball which adds to the net negative charge on the hailstone, as in Fig. 10–10. Thus the origin of lightning seems to depend on the thermoelectric property of ice.* Mason's conclusions are currently being tested to see how well they verify in the laboratory of the atmosphere.

---

* In a communication found in the *Bulletin of the American Meteorological Society*, **45**, 4 (April 1964), Leo Alpert, a well-known consulting meteorologist, reminds us that there are a few reports, sprinkled throughout meteorological literature, of lightning from clouds which contain no ice, i.e., warm clouds. Unfortunately most of the observations of such phenomena prior to 1963 are inadequate in some respect. Alpert cites details of a warm-cloud thunderstorm development on May 3, 1963, in southwestern Panama, which was examined throughout its lifetime both visually and by 3.2-centimeter radar. Many lightning strokes were observed. Alpert comments on the need for further active research, which undoubtedly will advance the whole theory of thunderstorm electricity.

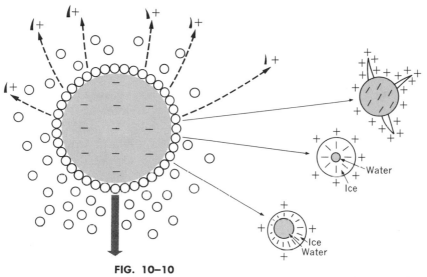

FIG. 10–10

Production of negative charge on hail pellets and positive charge on ice splinters.

Lightning

We shall now examine the details of the lightning stroke itself. We have already established the idea that ionization of the dielectric (the medium between the plates of the capacitor) follows when the charge on the capacitor plates exceeds a certain value. Let us look at this more closely. As a single negative ion is accelerated toward the positive plate, and a single positive ion is accelerated toward the negative plate, each acquires kinetic energy, some of which it imparts to the neighboring molecules with which it collides. At sea level the average distance a molecule can travel between collisions is very small, being of the order of one-millionth of a centimeter (actually 6.5×10^{-6} centimeter). If the strength of the electric field in the dielectric exceeds 30,000 volts/centimeter, the ions will acquire enough energy to produce pairs of charged particles, called ion pairs, as a result of the collision event; i.e., their energy will exceed that necessary to ionize the molecules they strike. Then each of these newly formed ions experiences the pull of the electric field, is accelerated, acquires energy, collides with a neutral molecule, and produces another ion pair. Ions are thus produced in geometric progression, which means that the production rate is so rapid that physicists use the term "avalanche" to describe the flow of charged particles. We mentioned 30,000 volts/centimeter as a limiting value. This is for dry air. In a cloud the value may drop to 10,000 volts/centimeter.

The normal field strength found between a convective cloud and the ground, or within the cloud, ranges between 100 and 1000 volts/centimeter. However, the violent turbulent motion in a cumulonimbus occasionally causes the field to increase beyond the critical value of 10,000. Then a negative charge, called the *pilot leader*, advances rapidly a hundred meters or so toward the positive (or less negative) center, forming an ionized path about the size of one's arm. A surge of negative charge proceeds down the ionized path, reinforcing the potential at the head. This movement is somewhat like that of the spearhead vehicles of an armored-attack group which spurt ahead at breakneck speed along a road in enemy territory until their supply of fuel runs out. As soon as a new supply is brought up by other carriers, the spearhead vehicles then proceed to make another thrust.

When, through a succession of surges of the pilot leader, the ionized path approaches the earth, a positive streamer leaves the sharp-pointed objects protruding from the earth (because the electric-field strength is greater around the sharp points). This streamer meets the pilot leader. A conducting path is established between cloud and ground. Up this path rushes the return stroke, more fully ionizing the channel. All the negative charge in the cloud then surges earthward through this path of low resistance and discharges the lowest section of the cloud. Sometimes, after the potential of the cloud rebuilds, a so-called *dart leader* reactivates the conducting path and the procedure is repeated. Thus there may be a few additional strokes which discharge higher portions of the cloud.

Thunder

And now what can be said about thunder? According to the physicist W. Remillard, the cloud-to-ground strokes which we have been describing take place very rapidly, in a few microseconds. As a result, a column of air is suddenly heated to temperatures in excess of $10,000°C$, as in an explosion. This causes a sudden buildup of pressure around the axis of the column, which moves outward at the speed of sound. (Sound, by definition, consists of a series of compressions and rarefactions moving through an elastic medium.) The ear interprets the arrival of this large-amplitude pressure wave as the familiar thunderclap.

It is known that thunder from near flashes begins with a crash, whereas thunder from far flashes begins with a rumble. This is due to the fact that the loudest clap originates near the junction of the lightning channel and the earth. Temperature gradients in the atmosphere during thunderstorm conditions are such as to cause the sounds to be refracted (bent) upward. Thus the sounds originating at the lower portions of the channel are heard by observers relatively near the flash. The same refraction causes the sounds from the entire channel to be lost to observers who are at distances from the flash exceeding 10–15 miles.

In general the duration of thunder is determined by the time required for sound originating in the upper part of the lightning stroke to reach the listener. Long duration of thunder is explained by the possible existence in the thundercloud of a sound-reflecting surface located near the top of the lightning channel and parallel to the earth's surface. This reflecting surface effectively doubles the length of the sound source, with the result that the duration of the thunder is considerably extended beyond what it would have been if there were no sound-reflecting surface.

Electrification by Convection

For many years observers have noted the heavy burst of rain which sometimes follows immediately after an overhead clap of thunder is heard. The inference is that there may be some significant cause-and-effect relationship between the lightning (and thus the thunder) and the sudden intensification of the precipitation. A number of cloud physicists led by B. Vonnegut and M. Brook are pursuing this line of investigation today. On the basis of a growing body of experimental evidence they suggest that electrification may be more the cause of precipitation than the result of it. They believe that positive ions, released in the atmosphere from the earth by point discharge, may be carried up into the interior of a growing cloud by means of updraft currents. Compensating downdrafts then carry negative ions into lower regions of the cloud. When the lightning stroke occurs, a localized region is produced in which there are many ions which charge the neighboring cloud droplets. These droplets move into the cloud and induce coalescence with other droplets carrying opposite charge, thus building up the large drops which fall after the thunder is heard.

This exposition of atmospheric electricity does not pretend to encompass the whole of this extraordinarily complex subject. It has been concerned with those facets of the subject which have direct meteorological relevance. We have seen that the thunderstorm is the principal agent in atmospheric electricity. In the next chapter we shall take a look at some of the progeny of the thunderstorm, which fall under the category of severe-weather phenomena.

CHAPTER **11**

Hail, Tornados, and Hurricanes

*We commence this chapter on severe storms
with the story of weather radar, because of its
importance as a research tool. We continue with
a description of the dynamics of the cumulonimbus cloud, mother of hail and the tornado.
Next we present the subject of hail, both
descriptively and analytically. Ludlam's model
of the hail-producing cumulonimbus is described.
The tornado and hurricane are then given
similar descriptive and analytic treatment.*

In this chapter we shall deal with three forms of severe storms: hail-producing thunderstorms, tornados, and hurricanes. There is no sharp break in continuity with the material in the previous chapter, for to describe hail we must concern ourselves with the characteristics of cumulonimbus buildups which produce lightning and thunder, i.e., thunderstorms. This is because such clouds are a necessary, but not a sufficient, condition of hail. In other words, it is necessary to have a thunderhead to produce hail, but all thunderheads do not produce hail.*

Before going further we must make a digression to become conversant with a new and powerful technique of gathering weather information from hitherto inaccessible regions. *Weather radar* now provides the meteorologist with "x-ray vision" which penetrates the interior of cloud masses and retrieves information about the water-ice content of the cloud. This capability has made weather radar as indispensable a tool to atmospheric scientists as the x-ray is to medical scientists. A large part of our new understanding of the structure of the cumulonimbus cloud mass, the tornado, and the hurricane comes from an analysis of information gathered by radar.

WEATHER RADAR

The origins of radar†—RAdio Detection And Ranging—go back to 1922 when A. H. Taylor and L. C. Young of the U.S. Navy Aircraft Radio Laboratory at Anacostia Naval Air Station near Washington, D.C. accidentally discovered that they could detect the presence of moving ships by high-frequency radio. The next step took place in 1925 when G. Breit and M. A. Tuve of the Carnegie Institution of Washington proposed the use of radio pulses for measuring the height of the ionosphere. A third major link in the discovery chain took place in 1930 when L. A. Hyland and L. C. Young discovered the detection of aircraft by radio. These developments were not radar, as yet.

The idea of pulse radar, involving the placing of transmitter and receiver close to each other, and using very short pulses of high power,

---

* This statement is not strictly correct, because small hail may fall from clouds which do not reach thunderstorm proportions, and though many thunderstorms may contain hail at some stage of their development, it may melt before reaching the ground. Because of the pinpoint nature of cumulus clouds, climatological hail statistics are bound to be unreliable; many showers do not choose to fall on the observation stations.

† The following facts are drawn from *The Origin of Radar,* by Robert Morris Page (Garden City, N.Y.: Doubleday, 1962).

was proposed in 1930, but nothing came of it because it seemed so far beyond the technological capability of the day. Four years later the idea came alive again as providing a means for developing an air warning system for large cities. With the stimulus of imminent conflict with Nazi Germany, the British in 1935 launched into an intensive development program. This resulted in a system of detection that may well have been the decisive factor in foiling German attempts to bring Britain to her knees.

The story of the further development of radar during World War II by the United States, and its successful use by surface ships and aircraft, is well known and need not be detailed here. Our particular concern is with a specific application of this idea, but we must preface this aspect of the story with a description of how radar works.

In the simplest terms radar operates on the principle of sending out from a transmitter in a known direction very powerful and short pulses of radio-frequency energy spaced widely apart. Weak pulses are then reflected back from objects which the pulses have "illuminated," and are picked up on a receiver which is in the same location as the transmitter.

When the sun's light illuminates an object of the dimensions of an airplane, perhaps two kilowatts of short-wavelength radiant energy enables the object to be seen by man's eyes from distances in excess of ten miles when the air is calm and clean. When it comes to illuminating such an object by electromagnetic energy of *radio wavelengths*, a prime consideration is that the wavelength of the radiation should be no greater than twice the smallest object if good reception is to be assured. This suggests a longest wavelength of 20–30 meters, which corresponds to a frequency of 15–10 megacycles (i.e., millions of cycles)/second.

If the object to be illuminated is a water drop instead of an airplane, it follows that electromagnetic waves of much shorter wavelength must be used; and this means higher operating frequencies.

The operating frequencies of weather radar are summarized in the following table.

TABLE 11–1

Frequency, megacycles (10^3)	Wavelength, cm	Name of band
30.0	1	K
10.0	3	X
6.0	5	C
3.0	10	S
1.5	20	L

The electromagnetic energy is generated in an electron tube called a *magnetron*. This is fed in pulses of microsecond duration, repeated 1000 times/second, to an antenna from which a narrow beam or "pencil" of energy is sent out at 3×10^8 meters/second, the speed of all electromagnetic radiation, including light.

When this beam encounters, or "illuminates," any foreign object, a fraction of the energy is scattered back along the beam, where it can be detected by a receiver, amplified, and transformed to give a visual signal.

Since short-wavelength radio waves travel essentially in straight lines, and the beam is well defined, accurate measurements may be made of azimuth and elevation angles. Also the distance in meters of the "target" may be determined quite simply by multiplying the time lapse in seconds between transmission and receipt of the pulse by 3×10^8, and dividing by two, since the total time is the time it takes the pulse to go to the target and return.

Three principal kinds of indicators are used in weather radar, depending on the kind of information desired. The A-scope or R-scope resembles a test oscilloscope. In this device, the beam of electrons scans from left to right horizontally across the face of the scope, showing a vertical deflection when signals reflected from the target are received. The height of the deflection is proportional to the strength of the signal. The most useful indicator is the plan-position indicator (PPI-scope). This is used on radar sets whose antennae rotate about a vertical axis and whose beam, as a radius vector, sweeps the area of a circle of which the transmitter is the center. The scope's electron beam scans successively at a fixed speed from the center of the oscilloscope to the outer edge. The stronger the return signal, the brighter the spot of light produced by the electron beam on the face of the scope.

The third means of display is the range-height indicator (RHI-scope). This is used with radars whose antennae rotate up and down about a horizontal axis. The strength of the return signal is indicated by the brightness of the electron spot. Schematic diagrams of these three scopes are shown in Fig. 11–1.

One of the crucial problems of weather radar is the efficiency with which the targets—cloud droplets, raindrops, hailstones, snowflakes—send back the electromagnetic energy with which they are illuminated.

Much of our understanding of the theory of scattering can be traced to the work of two theoretical physicists, the Englishman Lord Rayleigh and the German Gustave Mie. Rayleigh's concern was to explain the blue color of the sky. A little less than a hundred years ago he showed theoretically that small objects (of molecular size) scattered the sun's

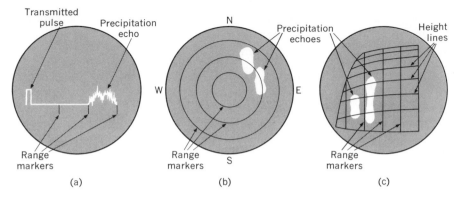

FIG. 11–1
Three common ways of displaying precipitation echoes: (a) A- or R-scope; (b) plan-position indicator (PPI-scope); (c) range-height indicator (RHI-scope). From *Radar Meteorology*, by Louis J. Battan. Copyright © 1959 by the University of Chicago. Published 1959. Second Impression 1960. Composed and printed by the University of Chicago Press, Chicago, Ill., U.S.A.

light which illuminated them more effectively in the blue wavelengths than in the red. In fact the scattering is proportional to the *inverse fourth power* of the wavelength of the illuminating radiation. Since the ratio of blue (0.4 micron) to red (0.75 micron) wavelength is about 1 to 2, this would mean the power of the scattered blue wavelengths would be 16 times that of the red. Thus we should expect the sky to appear blue. If we apply this reasoning to radar waves, the 5-centimeter waves should produce 16 times as much backscatter energy (from small spheres of a given size) as 10-centimeter waves. On the other hand, Lord Rayleigh's scattering law shows that the scattered power is proportional to the sixth power of the diameter of the scattering sphere for a particular wavelength. Comparing a droplet of 1-millimeter diameter with another of 2-millimeter diameter, we would find that the latter would scatter $(2/1)^6 = 2 \times 2 \times 2 \times 2 \times 2 \times 2 = 64$ times as much power. Other ratios show $(3/1)^6 = 729$, $(4/1)^6 = 4096$, and so on. These factors present a clear-cut mandate to use short-wavelength radar if one wishes to see small droplets. However, there is the complication of attenuation, or weakening, of the reflected signal. A cloud mass consists of a large aggregate of droplets. The shorter the wavelength, the greater the effect the aggregate of scattering spheres has in decreasing the outgoing and reflected power of the radiation. Theory shows that long wavelengths are less attenuated.[*]

---

[*] This, of course, is why sunsets and sunrises tend to be reddish in color. The blue radiation in the spectrum is attenuated more than the red as the light from the sun passes horizontally through the dusty atmosphere.

If short-wave radar should be used to see droplets, but long-wave radar must be used to get strong echoes back from clouds spread over a large horizontal area, a compromise is mandatory. This is why 10–20-centimeter radar sets (S- and L-Band) are used in observing large storm areas, whereas 1–3-centimeter sets (K- and X-Band) are more effective in analyzing individual clouds.

In order to give some idea of the numbers involved we cite an example used by L. Battan, a noted authority on weather radar. It can be shown that a raindrop of 1-millimeter diameter, at a range of 10 kilometers, backscatters 6×10^{-20} watt to the receiver of a 10-centimeter radar. This is below the 10^{-13}-watt level of threshold sensitivity of such a set and thus would not be detected. However, raindrops do not occur singly. On the average they occur in numbers of 100–1000/cubic meter.

Now consider a 300-meter pulse-length beam of 3 degrees in width at 10 kilometers distance filled with 500 drops/cubic meter. In a truncated cone 150 meters long at 10 kilometers there would be about 2×10^{10} drops. If the backscatter power from each were 6×10^{-20} watt, the average power from the rainstorm would be 12×10^{-10} watt, and this would be a detectable signal. Why was the figure of 150 meters used? Radar theory shows that all the droplets enclosed within a volume whose length is *one-half* a pulse length send back an echo to the receiver which arrives *at the same instant;* 150 meters is half a pulse length. No attenuation effects have been considered in this example; this is permissible if 10-centimeter (or greater) radar is used. See Fig. 11–2.*

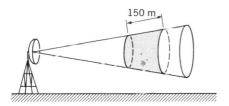

FIG. 11–2
Reflected power from all droplets in a truncated cone of 150-meter "altitude" reaches radar set at the same instant. The pulse length of the radar beam is 300 meters.

Since we will be discussing hail in the next section, we may ask whether radar is able to distinguish between an ice sphere and a water drop. The general answer to this question is affirmative, from the standpoint of both theory and experiment. However, the problem is a complex one which takes us back to the contribution of Gustave Mie. In 1908 he proposed a more general theory of scattering than Rayleigh's,

* From *Radar Observes the Weather,* by Louis J. Battan. Garden City, N.Y.: Doubleday, 1962. Copyright © 1962 by Educational Services Incorporated (Science Study Series). Reprinted by permission of Doubleday & Company.

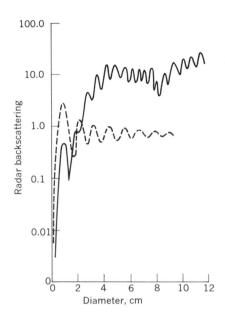

FIG. 11–3

Backscattering of energy from ice and water spheres. When a 3-centimeter radar is used, the returned power is proportional to the number on the vertical scale multiplied by the area of the scattering spherical particle. The dashed line is for water. From *Radar Observes the Weather*, by Louis J. Battan. Garden City, N.Y.: Doubleday, 1962. Copyright © 1962 by Educational Services Incorporated (Science Study Series). Reprinted by permission of Doubleday & Company, Inc.

which was restricted to particles much smaller than the wavelength of the radiation which illuminated them. The mathematics of Mie's theory was complex and lengthy, and it is only with the advent of the computer that it has been relatively easy to apply this theory to a variety of particular cases, such as the scattering ability of a sphere of ice, or a sphere of ice coated with a sheath of water (a melting hailstone). The curves, drawn in Fig. 11–3, summarize the results of applying Mie's theory to the cloud-physics problem. Note that for very small particles water backscatters better than ice, yet a single large hailstone can scatter many millions of times more power than a raindrop. With theoretical understanding it became possible to interpret the unusually strong echo received from some thunderstorms as resulting from the presence of hailstones.

Weather radar plays a very important role in helping the cloud physicist in his studies of the precipitation mechanism. We discussed the ice-crystal and the coalescence theory in an earlier chapter. One of the types of observational data which have substantiated the latter theory is that obtained from radar studies of cumulus and cumulonimbus clouds. In some convective clouds the echo associated with raindrops on the RHI-scope always lies below the freezing level. This is conclusive evidence that in such clouds the raindrop growth must have taken place by the coalescence process.

THUNDERSTORM DYNAMICS

Climatological data show that hail is unknown in the Tropics and in the Arctic. Other geographical areas, such as the centers of large land masses like Central Europe and the United States, and mountainous regions like Switzerland, experience about 10 devastating hailstorms per year. In contrast, Florida, with an average of 90 thunderstorm days per year, scarcely ever experiences hail. Evidently there is something different in degree, if not in kind, about a hail-producing thunderstorm that differentiates it from a non-hail-producing thunderstorm.

The perplexing fact is that in any given thunderstorm-prone region in the higher latitudes on a particular day there may be a severe thunderstorm with little associated hail, while on another day in the same location the thunderhead may produce a heavy fall of hail.

In order to put the problem in perspective, let us look more closely at the dynamics of the thunderstorm cloud mass.

Thunderstorm Project

What we know today about the internal structure of thunderstorms comes in large part from ground-based and aircraft observations obtained by the Thunderstorm Project, an extensive study undertaken jointly by the U.S. Weather Bureau and several other government agencies between 1946 and 1949. Using Thunderstorm Project data, Horace R. Byers and Roscoe R. Braham of the University of Chicago showed that the typical thunderstorm is an agglomeration of "cells." These cells, which are between one and a few miles across, contain vigorous chimneys of rising or descending air, i.e., updrafts and downdrafts. The characteristic lifetime of an individual cell is half an hour to one hour, while a large thunderstorm, as a cluster of continually evolving cells, may persist for up to twelve hours. From this and subsequent smaller investigations has come a fairly complete understanding of the life cycle of the thunderstorm cell, which we now summarize in terms of three stages: the *cumulus stage*, the *mature stage*, and the *dissipating stage*, shown in Fig. 11–4.

In the cumulus stage the cell is characterized by an updraft throughout. This has a width of about one mile, is strongest at the top of the cell, and increases in strength with time. Converging air feeds the updraft both from the surface and from the unsaturated environmental air surrounding the cell. Temperatures inside the cloud are greater than those outside the cloud. Though charge separation is taking place, there is no lightning.

Altitude, ft

Temperature, °C

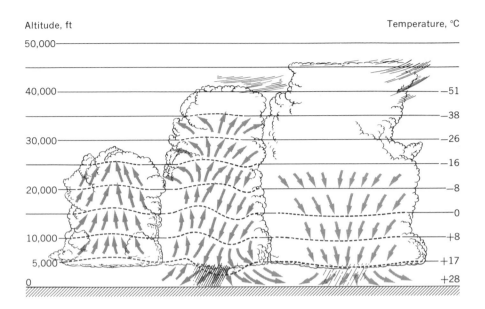

FIG. 11–4

Three stages in the life cycle of a thunderstorm cell. From left to right: the cumulus stage, the mature stage, and the dissipating stage. The cumulus stage is characterized by updrafts throughout. The mature stage has both updrafts and downdrafts and produces heavy rain (and perhaps hail). The dissipating stage has weak downdrafts throughout.

The mature stage is reached when rain starts to fall from the bottom of the cloud. One finds both updrafts and downdrafts in the lower half of the cell. The downdraft is induced by the precipitation, but once started, can continue without the frictional drive. The updrafts reach their maximum speed in the upper part of the cell, sometimes exceeding 200 miles/hour. Temperatures in the updraft are higher than those outside the cloud, while temperatures in the downdraft are lower than those outside. The reason is that in the former case, the energy release of latent heat overcompensates for expansional cooling, and in the latter case, evaporation of the rain overcompensates for compressional heating. Electrical activity reaches its climax during the mature stage. Turbulence in the cloud is most intense. The heaviest rain (and perhaps hail) falls from the cloud. Frequently the tops of thunderstorms rise to 12–13 miles, penetrating the tropopause. Rain, carried aloft in the strong updrafts, may be encountered well above the level of the freezing isotherm.

When the updraft finally ceases, the dissipating stage begins. As the rainfall dies out, the strength of the downdraft in the lower portions of the cell diminishes. The below-normal temperatures gradually rise and the cloud slowly disintegrates into a series of stratified layers.

The use of radar in the analysis of the buildup of a thunderstorm cloud verifies the idea that the larger cloud mass is an aggregate of smaller cells in various stages of development. Vertically scanning radar often shows the growth of a narrow "echo tower" which builds to a great height over an average period of 23 minutes. One tower follows another, each penetrating to greater heights in the active growth period of the storm. The upward growth rate of the tops of echoes in convective clouds is 10–20 miles/hour, but in the more active thunderstorms it can be several times as great.

Propagation

Two scientists, Newton and Fankhauser, have more recently been studying the movement of multicelled storms. For the central Great Plains area they found that the pattern of development and decay of the cells is one of the most important factors governing the movement of the storm as a whole. In the typical case the cells move toward the northeast. New cells form to the right of existing cells and old cells dissipate on the left. Thus propagation results in a movement of the thunderstorm as a whole toward the right of the path of movement of its individual cells. This is shown in Fig. 11–5.

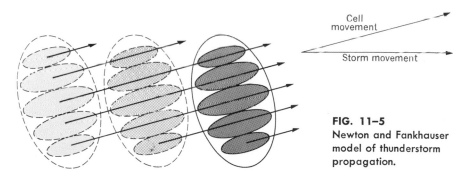

FIG. 11–5
Newton and Fankhauser model of thunderstorm propagation.

As the storm moves through the lower-level air mass, where most of the available water vapor is concentrated, it sweeps up moisture, a certain proportion of which is converted into precipitation. Newton and Fankhauser hypothesized that the amount of water rained out is roughly proportional to the storm area and thus to the square of its diameter.

The quantity of water vapor carried into the storm by low-level winds is, however, directly proportional to the cloud's diameter. The vapor intercepted is also proportional to the velocity of the low-level winds relative to the size of storm. For the moisture supply to balance the loss by precipitation, this relative velocity must be greater for a large than a small storm. The relative velocity is increased if the storm moves to the right of the mean wind direction, and diminished if it moves to the left. Though this model describes typical behavior, and actual thunderstorms may deviate from it, it represents a definite step toward the goal of short-period thunderstorm forecasting.

Having summarized the major outlines of the life cycle of a cumulonimbus thunderstorm cloud, we now turn our attention to hail.

HAIL

Hailstones are transparent or partially opaque particles of ice which range in size from sweet-pea seeds to baseballs, and in shape from spheres to rounded cones (pear-shape). A feature of many, but not all, of the larger hailstones is that of an "onion-skin" arrangement with alternating layers of clear and whitish (opaque) ice.

The following table gives a frequency distribution of the sizes of the largest hailstones observed in the Denver, Colorado, area between 1949 and 1955.* This is presented as a typical example of what might be expected in a hail-prone region.

Diameter of largest hailstones	Number of cases
Grain (to $\frac{1}{4}$ in.)	10
Currant ($\frac{1}{4}$ in.)	122
Pea ($\frac{1}{2}$ in.)	282
Grape ($\frac{3}{4}$ in.)	149
Walnut (1–1$\frac{1}{4}$ in.)	38
Golf ball (1$\frac{3}{4}$–2 in.)	26
Tennis ball (2$\frac{1}{2}$–3 in.)	4

The largest authentically recorded hailstones in the United States fell during a storm at Potter, Nebraska, on July 6, 1928. One stone measured 15 inches in circumference and almost 5$\frac{1}{2}$ inches in diameter, and weighed 11$\frac{1}{2}$ pounds! These stones fell 10–15 feet apart and completely buried themselves where they struck soft ground. They were individual stones with the typical concentric layers of ice formed around a single center.

---

* Reported by W. Boynton Beckwith (1956), United Air Lines.

One of the significant steps toward increased understanding of the fine details of the phenomenon has been a technique of analysis developed by Swiss cloud physicists. Hailstones are collected, kept at below-freezing temperatures, then cut in paper-thin equatorial sections. These sections are analyzed with polarized light, that is, light in which the electric-field vector vibrates only in one plane. The analysis shows that an individual hailstone consists of a large number of ice crystals of different sizes and distinctly different colors.* The large crystals are interpreted as corresponding to regions of clear ice, while the aggregate of small crystals is interpreted as corresponding to the opaque regions. See Fig. 11–6. (The milky white appearance of the opaque regions is caused by the presence of many small air bubbles trapped between the small ice crystals.)

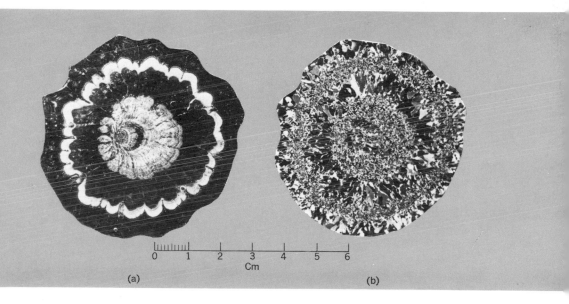

(a)   (b)

FIG. 11–6
Thin section cut through growth center of a giant hailstone. The first photograph (a), taken using reflected light, shows bubble structure with milky zone appearing white and transparent ice appearing black. The second photograph (b), taken using transmitted polarized light, shows crystal fabric, with individual crystallites appearing as separate tones. Courtesy K. A. Browning, Office of Aerospace Research, U.S. Air Force, AFCRL 65-695(1) Sept. 1965, Special Reports No. 32, p. 291.

---

* The explanation of the colors involves the theory of physical optics and is beyond the scope of this book.

Every hailstone, in fact, carries with it its own life history. The task of the cloud physicist is to take this life history and work backward from it to a model of the thunderhead which enables him to account for the observed development. It becomes clear that the opaque layers are formed when the hailstone encounters a region of many small supercooled droplets which freeze on impact. The clear layers must then be formed by the stone's encounter with large supercooled raindrops. When these impact with the hailstone, they spread and surround it with a sheath of water which freezes more slowly as the latent heat is conducted away. As a consequence of the slow freezing rate, the air dissolved in the water is "squeezed out" and escapes.

When one measures the mass distribution of the clear ice and the opaque ice in the various layers of the stone, one can then infer that the growing hailstone must have spent x seconds in a particular environment of large supercooled drops and y seconds in another particular environment of small supercooled droplets.

Numbers are impressive at this point. We saw previously that it takes about a million cloud droplets to make up the mass of water contained in an average-size raindrop. Extending the argument, we find it takes about a billion small cloud droplets to form a pea-sized hailstone and a million million small cloud droplets to form a hailstone of baseball size; i.e., it takes one to ten thousand large raindrops.

The growth pattern of a hailstone is controlled by its time of residence, so to speak, in different water environments within the cloud. The time interval is intimately related to the strength and duration of updrafts in the cloud. Recent evidence indicates that the strong updraft must persist for as long as an hour.

We have previously given terminal velocities for water spheres of different diameters. (See Table 9–1.) If the terminal velocity of an ice ball of 2 inches in diameter is 100 feet/second, and if the ice ball is to remain at a constant height, it must be embedded in a mass of air which is rising at 100 feet/second. The rate at which it will be carried aloft in the cloud will then be the difference between the updraft and the terminal velocity. As was pointed out in the previous chapter, growth by coalescence takes place when some fraction of the droplets in the "cylinder of vision" of the stone strike and freeze.

Schumann (1938) produced the first really quantitative treatment of hailstone growth. F. H. Ludlam, colleague of B. J. Mason at Imperial College, advanced Schumann's theory by the introduction of experimentally determined values of the drop-size distribution and updraft velocities. As a result Ludlam has given us one of the best models of the hail-producing thunderstorm.

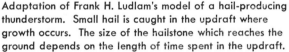

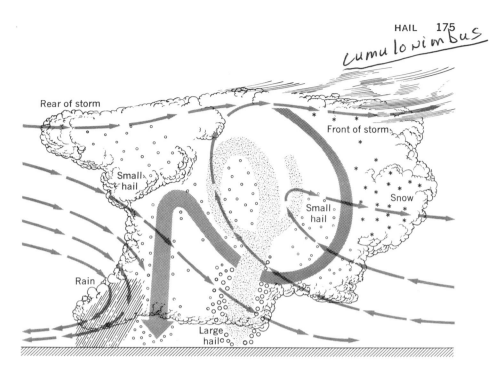

FIG. 11–7
Adaptation of Frank H. Ludlam's model of a hail-producing
thunderstorm. Small hail is caught in the updraft where
growth occurs. The size of the hailstone which reaches the
ground depends on the length of time spent in the updraft.

This model involves a cumulonimbus development in an area in which
strong upper winds overlie a deep, moist lower layer of air. In the mid-
west region of the United States a deep column of warm, moist air having its origin in the Gulf of Mexico is sometimes topped by a dry westerly
current which reaches jet stream velocities. This situation is known to
forecasters to be favorable for hail-producing thunderstorms, and corresponds to the requirements of Ludlam's model (or vice versa).

Because of the increase in horizontal wind speed with elevation, the
principal updraft column in the thunderhead tilts in the direction of
propagation of the storm, as shown in Fig. 11–7. If an embryo hailstone,
consisting of a central ice crystal covered by rime (frozen cloud droplets), gets caught in the updraft column, it will start its period of rapid
growth by accretion. Its eventual size will be determined by how long it
manages to stay within the updraft column. Its structure will be determined by how many times it falls out and is caught up in it once more.
One can see that there exist in a Ludlam-type hail-producing cumulonimbus many possibilities for different growth rates and forms. This
accounts for the variety of hailstones, as described earlier.

THE TORNADO

Of all the natural calamities confronting man, the tornado is most like the man-made disaster resulting from aerial bombardment of civilian populations in time of war. The lack of forewarning, the sudden explosive fury of the winds, the brief duration of onslaught, the complete helplessness of a community when disaster strikes, and the desolation and destruction which follow—these features of a bomb raid are also characteristic of the tornado.

A tornado—or "twister" as it is sometimes called—is undoubtedly the most awe-inspiring atmospheric phenomenon found in the mid-latitude zone. The distinguishing feature is the menacing funnel cloud extending earthward from the base of a cumulonimbus cloud which sometimes develops a "mamma" structure at its base. The funnel can vary in shape: it can be a narrow inverted cone, a vertical cylinder, an hourglass, or a long twisting rope. Sometimes the funnel is distinct, as in Plate 11–1; at other times it is obscured in dust and/or rain squalls. The funnel cloud moves cross-country at an average speed of 30–40 miles/hour. The length of the path is a little more than 10 miles. One of the longest paths on record in Kansas was that of the tornado which struck Hutchinson on May 8, 1927 and traveled 102 miles. Some storms in states farther east are reported to have traveled 200–300 miles. Since the width of the funnel cloud seldom exceeds one mile, and is more often of the order of a few hundred feet, the center rarely passes directly over a meteorological observation station. Thus accurate values of the central pressure are difficult to obtain. From the evidence that does exist, both direct and indirect, it is believed that the central pressure may drop dramatically to values as low as 60–80 percent of normal atmospheric pressure, i.e., 600–800 millibars. Air sucked into the vortex is cooled by expansion and brought to saturation, with the result that clouds are formed, outlining the funnel shape of the vortex. As the droplets grow larger, and dust and debris is sucked into the circulation, the funnel takes on its black, ominous appearance.

PLATE 11–1
Tornado funnel.
Courtesy ESSA, National Severe Storms Laboratory.

Because of the excessively strong pressure gradients built up around the low-pressure core, a narrow ring of unbelievably strong winds develops. Peak wind velocities have to be estimated from the aftereffects because no gage has survived to record them. Illustrative of the amazing aftereffects is the straw which pierces a heavy plank. It can be shown physically that winds of 300–400 miles/hour are necessary to give a frail object such penetrating ability.

In addition to the devastation caused by the strong winds, much damage to dwellings results from the rapid pressure change which accompanies the passage of the storm. Buildings literally explode. A few numbers will show how this is possible. If we assume that it takes but one minute for the funnel to pass a given small area (and this is a reasonable time for a narrow funnel moving at about 30 miles/hour), the maximum pressure fall would occur in half a minute. Let us consider dropping the atmospheric pressure by 2 inches of mercury on the outside of a box-shaped barn. Two inches of mercury would correspond to approximately one pound/square inch. If the roof of the barn were 20 feet by 30 feet, its area would be 86,400 square inches. Therefore, since $F = pA$, there would be an upward thrust on the interior of the roof of 86,400 pounds, or 4.32 tons! Suffice it to say that the roof would have to be very strongly nailed down to keep it from flying off, and the building itself would have to be anchored securely to the foundations to prevent its being lifted bodily into the air (as happened to the house occupied by Dorothy, the young heroine of Wizard of Oz fame).

There are a few, and only a few, eye-witness reports on record from reliable observers who have seen the interior of the funnel. One of the most graphic is that of Milton Tabor who happened to be with a group of students just east of Lincoln, Nebraska, in the late afternoon of March 23, 1913, when a tornado originated over their heads. He describes the sight as follows:

"The tornado cloud formed near where we were enjoying a picnic and whirled furiously high in the air straight over our heads. We looked up into what appeared to be an enormous hollow cylinder, bright inside with lightning flashes but black as blackest night all around. The noise was like ten million bees, plus a roar that beggars description." (*Weatherwise*, April, 1949)

Before we attempt to describe how and why tornados form, we need to look at the "where" and "when" factors which may provide clues. Figure 11–7 shows that the tornado is primarily a phenomenon of the Great Plains and eastern United States. Iowa, Arkansas, Kansas, Mississippi, Alabama, and Missouri lead in frequency of tornados *per year*

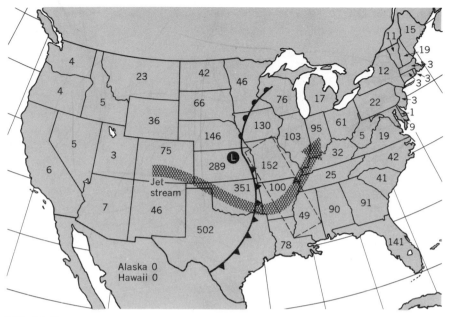

FIG. 11–8

The rectangular area is the favored region for development of tornados. The figures are numbers of tornados reported in the period 1960–1964.

per unit area, ranging from 2.7 to 1.0 in that order. Tornados are relatively unknown west of the Continental Divide. When they do occur they tend to be small and short-lived.

In the Great Plains states the preferred time of formation of tornados lies between 1500 and 2100 hours (3–9 p.m.), with a peak between 1700 and 1900 (5–7 p.m.). On the other hand, in the southeastern states one can expect tornados to occur at any time of day or night, with only slightly greater frequency in the late afternoon.

With respect to season, the period of maximum occurrence starts in early spring in Mississippi and Alabama, and by May and June has advanced north-northwestward to Kansas. In Florida the occurrence is evenly distributed throughout the year.

The forecaster knows from his experience that tornados usually develop in the southeast region (or warm sector) of a low-pressure area, and they tend to travel parallel (from southwest to northeast) to the well-marked cold front which bounds the cold air to the west. His upper-air charts often show the presence of a well-defined jet stream in the middle troposphere, whose direction (usually southwest-northeast) seems to determine that of the funnel. See Fig. 11–8.

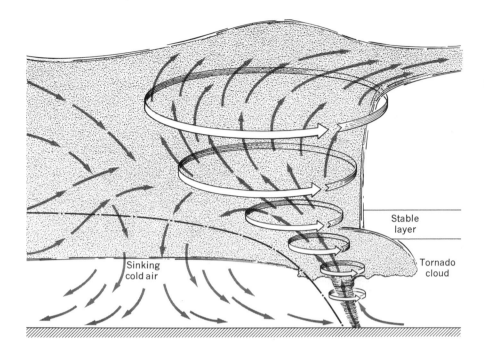

Stable
layer

Sinking
cold air

Tornado
cloud

FIG. 11-9
Sketch of a tornado thunderstorm. Courtesy
J. R. Fulks, Report No. 4, National Severe Storms
Project, U.S. Weather Bureau.

There is some evidence that smaller low-pressure areas of only a few miles in diameter within the large low-pressure region are significant in the genesis of tornados. Investigations of such areas, known as "tornado cyclones," indicate they may possess an initial counterclockwise rotational motion and corresponding angular momentum which, in conjunction with stability factors, initiate the violent tornadic circulation.

We have shown that the cumulonimbus cloud is an outgrowth of active convection in unstable and moisture-laden air (technically, convectively unstable air). Instability in an air mass can be released in three different ways: (a) by heating from below, (b) by cooling from above, and (c) by forced ascent of a mass of air in which dry air overlies moist air. If it were conceivable that all three causative factors were to operate simultaneously, this would be likely to result in that violent convection which generates the tornado-spawning cumulonimbus. Figure 11-9 shows a suggested flow pattern which may exist in a tornado thunderstorm.

Heating from below reaches its maximum effect in the late afternoon (condition *a*); sudden cooling from above results when there is an intrusion from the west of a relatively cold air stream which may shear off the upper portion of the surface layer of warm, moist Gulf air (condition *b*); the presence of circulation within the "tornado cyclone" causes general ascent, which releases the convective instability (condition *c*). It so happens that the high frequency of tornado occurrence in Kansas and Iowa results from the favorable location of these areas for a conjunction of these three conditions.

In an effort to understand the dynamics of the tornado some scientists attempt to simulate the storm through laboratory models. One of the most sophisticated pieces of work, by J. S. Turner of Woods Hole Oceanographic Institute, has yielded valuable conclusions, which we summarize. Pointing out that the condensation funnel and the debris kicked up from the ground are very poor tracers of air motion, Turner concludes from his studies that the whole of the *vertical* circulation is confined to a cylinder around the axis. Near the axis is a region of upflow, and an annular ring surrounding this contains the compensating downflow. The vortex is driven from the cloud region. Inflow takes place at the bottom of the funnel.

One of the important uses of weather radar today is in identifying and tracking severe storms such as tornados and hurricanes. We have already indicated that tornados do not usually form in the absence of severe thunderstorms. Unfortunately no positive means of identifying a tornado by use of a radar picture has yet been found. Some tornados have been associated with a "6"-shaped echo on the right rear portion of thunderstorm echoes on the PPI-scope, as in Plate 11–2. But tornados are also known to have formed in the absence of such echoes.

G. N. Brancato's report of the 1959 St. Louis tornado as given in *Weatherwise* (April, 1959) is presented here to give the reader a sense of the sequence of events in a tornado.

"The tornado struck the outskirts shortly after 0200 and hit the center of the city between 0213–0220. The tornado was preceded during the night by a series of intense thunderstorms which produced between one and three inches of rain over the area and caused flash floods in many of the streams in the greater St. Louis area. By 2300 the heavy rains and most of the intense thunderstorm activity had moved to the east of St. Louis, and there were breaks in the clouds with stars clearly visible for a period of time. At about 0100 the St. Louis radar began to pick up a squall line approaching at a speed of approximately 30 knots. As the squall line approached, it was evident from the echoes that there was rather intense thunderstorm activity. Between 0100 and 0200 a few reports were received

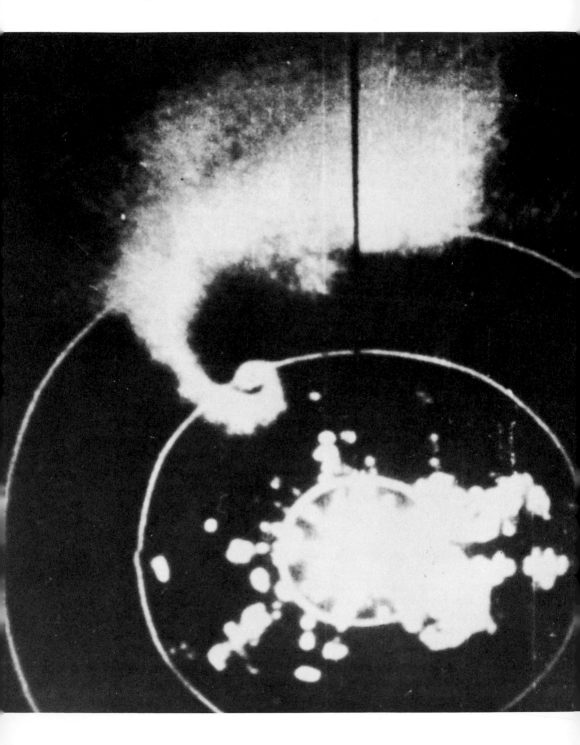

from Severe Weather Observers in the path of the squall line reporting winds estimated at 40 to 50 knots and some hail. A severe thunderstorm warning had been in effect since the preceding evening and extended until 0230 for the St. Louis area. The thunderstorms were occurring in advance of a Pacific cold front in warm, moist, and very unstable air. . . .

Although the squall line was apparently moving at the rate of approximately 35 mph, the tornado moved across the city at a rate of 60–65 mph. In its travel across the county and city, it dipped down . . . for a distance of several blocks unroofing houses and causing considerable damage. A little further . . . it toppled the 575-foot steel tower of KTVI. . . . When the work of sifting through the ruins was completed the following damage and casualties were reported.

Persons killed	21
Persons with major injuries or illnesses	72
Persons with minor injuries	273
Total families suffering loss	3036
Total property damage, approximately	$10,000,000"

At times conditions of extreme atmospheric instability are found over masses of water. If a funnel cloud happens to develop downward from the cloud to the water surface, the lowered atmospheric pressure in the vortex will cause rapid evaporation, and large masses of water will be sucked up into the circulation. Such a funnel cloud is commonly referred to as a *waterspout*.

Nature produces a variety of intense local vortex-type storms. The *dust-devil* whirlwind of desert and dry plains regions is a consequence of intense local heating which sets off violent convective currents.

An unusual case reported by Sigurdor Thorarinsson and Bernard Vonnegut (see, e.g., *Bulletin of the American Meteorological Society*, August, 1964) is that of the underwater volcanic eruption some twenty miles south of Iceland which formed a new island, now named Surtsey. During the first ten days of formation of the island in late November, 1963, vortices were observed forming downwind from the island underneath the volcanic cloud, as seen in Plate 11–3. These took all possible forms.

PLATE 11–2
Hook echo associated with the Meridian, Kansas, tornado of May 19, 1960, as seen on Topeka radar scope at 1831 CST. Distance between range markers is five nautical miles. Courtesy ESSA, National Severe Storms Laboratory.

It appeared that their formation depended on the intensity of the eruption and the wind. Though most vortices seemed to rotate in a counterclockwise sense, some rotated in the opposite sense. As the explosive nature of the eruption diminished, the number of funnel clouds also decreased. Pictures of these vortices show ash from the volcanic plume acting as a marker of the descending air. Such visual confirmation of Turner's ideas is not usually available in tornados.

It is instructive to view the tornado problem from the point of view of energy. Any explosive event in nature results from the sudden release of an excessive buildup of potential energy. The trigger may be man-activated, or it may be released naturally. This event may be an H-bomb explosion, the eruption of a volcano or a geyser—or a tornado. We have already seen that the extratropical cyclone is one of nature's favorite large-scale ways of dissipating the buildup of potential energy which takes place when cold air and warm air are brought into juxtaposition by the larger circulation patterns. The tornado is an extremely concentrated elixir of the same ingredients. The injection of cold air above a moisture-laden, and thus energy-packed, air mass which possesses some rotation represents a condition which nature simply cannot abide. The way out is a rapid generation of a great amount of energy of motion (i.e., wind), restricted to a few cubic miles in space. Because of this restriction, the wind must begin to circulate rapidly, and in so doing, it generates the tornado vortex. This outburst of kinetic energy is rapidly dissipated through friction as heat energy. Thus the atmosphere in this small volume is enabled to return to a relatively stable condition. (It should be pointed out that, as yet, there is no generally accepted theoretical treatment of the development and maintenance of the low-pressure vortex.)

It is extremely difficult to measure the energy release of a tornado quantitatively. Estimates have been made of heating rates resulting from fires in which a known amount of fuel was consumed and a whirlwind resulted. This seems to be of the order of 10^{10} joules/second. One estimate of the energy release in the early stages of the Surtsey eruption is of the order of 10^6 joules/second. One speculates that the energy release in a major tornado would exceed even this value.

PLATE 11–3
Volcanic cloud over Surtsey Island during the early days of formation in November 1963.
Note the multiple vortices under the volcanic cloud extending to the ocean surface.
The line on the surface is probably a windblown streak of tephra floating on the water.
Photo courtesy U.S. Navy and B. Vonnegut.

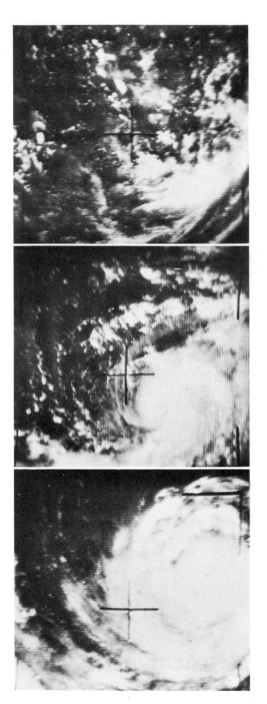

(a) Disturbed area

(b) Tropical storm

(c) Strong typhoon

PLATE 11-4
Three stages in the development
of a typhoon (hurricane).
Courtesy ESSA, Weather Bureau.

HURRICANES

Tropical cyclones which have reached certain degrees of intensity are known as *hurricanes* in the Atlantic Ocean, the Caribbean Sea, the Gulf of Mexico, and the eastern North Pacific Ocean (off the coast of Mexico); as *typhoons* in the western North Pacific; and as *cyclones* over most of the South Pacific Ocean and the Indian Ocean. Locally in the Philippines these storms are called *baguios* and in Australia *willy-willies.* All of them have the same conditions of origin, structure, and behavior.

A tropical cyclone starts out as a *tropical disturbance* in which there is a slight surface circulation and perhaps one closed isobar. When the wind increases to about 20 knots and there is more than one closed isobar around the center, it is called a *tropical depression.* When the wind rises to more than 34 knots, and there are several closed isobars, it becomes known as a *tropical storm.* If the winds exceed 64 knots (74 miles/hour), it is classified as a *hurricane* or *typhoon* or *cyclone* (depending on location). See Plate 11–4.

Hurricanes occur principally in the months from June through October. Those which occur early and late in the season are most likely to originate over the western Atlantic, the Caribbean, or the Gulf of Mexico, while those of "midseason," i.e., late August and September, most frequently originate between the West Indies and the eastern Atlantic.

Times of development in other principal geographical areas are: (a) North Pacific Ocean off the west Coast of Mexico—June through November, (b) North Pacific Ocean from longitude 170E westward to China—May through December, (c) South Pacific Ocean from east of Australia to longitude 140W—December through April.

Since 1953 the Weather Bureau has used girls' names to identify hurricanes. No reference is intended to persons, living or dead. Experience has shown that the use of girls' names is an aid to clear communication. In 1960 a semipermanent list of four sets of names in alphabetical order was compiled. The first hurricane of the 1965 season is Anna, in 1966 it is Alma, and so on. Successive storms are given successive names on the list. In 1969 the cycle of names repeats. The list of names (with blanks for Q, U, X, Y, and Z for lack of names) is given below.

1966   Alma, Becky, Celia, Dorothy, Ella, Flossy, Greta, Hallie, Inez, Judith, Kendra, Lois, Marsha, Noreen, Orpha, Patty, Rena, Sherry, Thora, Vicky, Wilma

1967   Arlene, Beulah, Cindy, Debra, Edith, Flora, Ginny, Helena, Irene, Janice, Kristy, Laura, Margo, Nona, Orchid, Portia, Rachel, Sandra, Terese, Verna, Wallis

1968   Abby, Brenda, Cleo, Dora, Ethel, Florence, Gladys, Hilda, Isabell, Janet, Katy, Lila, Molly, Nita, Odette, Paula, Roxie, Stella, Trudy, Vesta, Winny

1969   Anna, Betsy, Carol, Debbie, Elena, Frances, Gerda, Holly, Inga, Jenny, Kara, Laurie, Martha, Netty, Orva, Peggy, Rhoda, Sadie, Tanya, Virgy, Wenda

Hurricanes develop in low latitudes where the Coriolis force is very small. The embryo storm is usually found in a trough in the easterly air stream. In the early and middle stages of its development it encounters only tropical and equatorial air masses, which are very similar in the lowest altitudes (up to 10,000 feet). There are no fronts, in the extratropical sense. See Fig. 11–10 for a summary of the genesis regions of Atlantic hurricanes.

A mature hurricane is a circular storm which generates destructive winds extending 250–300 miles from the center. The highest wind speeds are found in a narrow ring extending 20–30 miles from the center, and in this region they may reach 150 miles/hour, with some higher gusts.

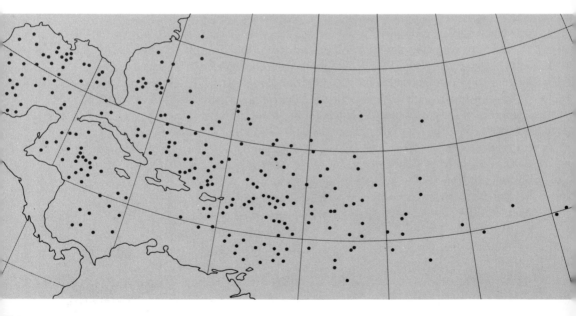

FIG. 11–10
Locations where tropical cyclones reached hurricane intensity, 1901–1957.   From G. E. Dunn and B. I. Miller, *Atlantic Hurricanes*, 2nd ed., Baton Rouge: Louisiana State University Press, 1964, by permission.

Accompanying the strong winds are extensive cloud and squally weather concentrated in spiral bands which pinwheel out from the center of the storm. At the very center of the storm there is a small core 5–20 miles across, called the *eye*. The winds in the eye range from dead calm to light breezes. Whereas the cumulonimbus clouds in the wall surrounding the eye extend vertically to 35,000–45,000 feet, the eye is generally free of clouds except for scattered to broken stratocumulus and fractostratus. Cirrus and cirrostratus can be observed at high elevations overlying the eye. Refer to Fig. 11–11.

What are the conditions for development of this storm? We recall that the extratropical wave cyclone develops because of the presence of cold and warm air masses in juxtaposition. But in the Tropics there is only one air mass; therefore the cause must be different. The air on the low-latitude side of the great oceanic high-pressure systems moves westward over thousands of miles of ocean. In the eastern end of the ocean basin the tropical air is topped by rather warm and dry air. This produces an inversion which has the effect of limiting vertical development

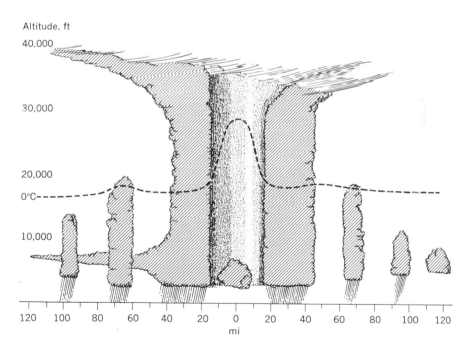

FIG. 11–11
Schematic cross section taken through a tropical cyclone (i.e., hurricane, typhoon). Typical isotherm shows the result of sinking and warming air in the core. Clouds beyond the central squall area arrange themselves in spiral bands.

of the trade-wind cumulus clouds to 6000–8000 feet. But in the western end of the ocean basin the inversion level is much weaker and is found at higher elevations. As a result, the low-level convective clouds have an opportunity to grow to much greater heights. This is why hurricanes are a phenomenon of the western ocean basin.

Hurricanes are born in one of the so-called easterly waves which are found in the trade-wind circulation moving slowly westward. This wave is an inverted trough. As one moves through the wave from east to west, the wind veers from easterly to southeasterly; then, as one passes the trough line, the wind backs to northeasterly. Because the trade-wind inversion is broken down in the trough, swelling cumulus and even cumulonimbus clouds develop along the eastern side of the trough and produce a region of squally weather. An easterly wave of large amplitude with an associated region of cumulonimbus activity is the seedbed of a tropical depression which may develop into a hurricane. One of the questions which intrigue specialists in tropical meteorology is what causes some depressions to spawn a hurricane while others do not. It appears that the answer to this question is directly related to the development of the *warm* core possessed by all hurricanes, for it has been observed that the more intense the storm, the warmer is the core. Sinking air produces the anomalies which, level for level, in a mature storm, range from 5°C at about 10,000 feet to as much as 10°C at 30,000 feet.

We suggest that a combination of many factors must be "right" for a depression to move into the "big leagues" and become a full-blown hurricane: cumulus activity must have pumped water vapor into high levels, the upper-air circulation must be favorable to generate the sinking motion which eventually will become the warm core, the latitude must be neither too low nor too high, and so on.

In the mature storm, warm moist air spirals in toward the center at low levels outside the eye wall. This circular motion of air within 30–40 miles of the eye persists to great heights. This motion feeds the storm and renews its supplies with unexpended sources of water-vapor fuel, which is released in the form of heat energy as the water vapor in the rising air condenses. In the upper layers of the troposphere there is a reversal of wind direction, and the air spirals away from the center of the storm.

While still in low latitudes, the eastward motion of the center is very slow, averaging about 10 miles/hour. As the storm recurves northward (to the right of its motion), it picks up forward speed and then may move as fast as 50 miles/hour. The tracks and rates of movement of individual storms vary as much from the average as human individuals differ from "the average human."

When the storm moves over a land area it is cut off from its source of fuel, experiences greater frictional forces due to the terrain, and consequently starts to dissipate. This period of dissipation may extend over several days, during which excessive falls of 5–10 inches of precipitation are recorded.

The greatest destructive force of the hurricane is the high water, or *storm surge*, often associated with the storm as it crosses a coastline. After fifty years' experience with storms, we can now forecast (within a foot or so) the height of the surge, if we know the difference in pressure near the center of the hurricane and at a point outside. If the point of entry along the coastline is known (and thus the lay of the land), it is possible to determine in advance the extent of flooding, so that appropriate evacuation measures can be taken.

Most hurricanes recurve while still at sea and only a few merchant ships feel their fury. However, a few storms each season pass over inhabited land masses and leave extensive destruction of property and (sometimes) loss of life. In order to minimize the damage and particularly the hazard to life, the U.S. Hurricane Warning Service was established in 1935. The prime function of the service was, and is, to facilitate prompt exchange of weather information. Miami, Florida, has been designated as the official coordinating center.

The first requirement which must be met for increased accuracy of hurricane forecasts is more precise information about all aspects of the storms, especially while they are still at sea. One of the most significant means of gathering such information is that of aerial reconnaissance flights. This procedure has been used systematically since 1944. Regular flights are carried out on command from Puerto Rico by the Navy Airborne Early Warning Squadron 4 and the U.S. Air Force Detachment No. 3, 55th Reconnaissance Squadron, operating from Bermuda. The several objectives of these flights include obtaining a "fix" on the location of the center, measurement of the minimum pressure, height of the clouds, strength of the winds, etc.

As soon as new instruments have become operational, they are put to use. For instance, a chain of weather radars now lines the coast from Brownsville, Texas, to New England. These keep surveillance on any storm within 200 miles of the coastline. Information from these radars is teletyped to the Hurricane Center where it is incorporated in the forecasts and advisory messages are issued from this office.

In addition to ground-based radar, each of the research aircraft is fitted with airborne radar, by means of which the pilot can avoid the hard cores of the storm, which because of their turbulence represent undue hazard to flight.

PLATE 11–5
Hurricane Cleo as photographed by Tiros VII on August
26, 1964 at 1121 EST. The eye is SSE of Miami,
Florida. Northern Florida is visible in the photograph.
Compare this picture of Cleo with the radar PPI-scope
picture taken only 11 hours later. Photo courtesy ESSA,
Weather Bureau.

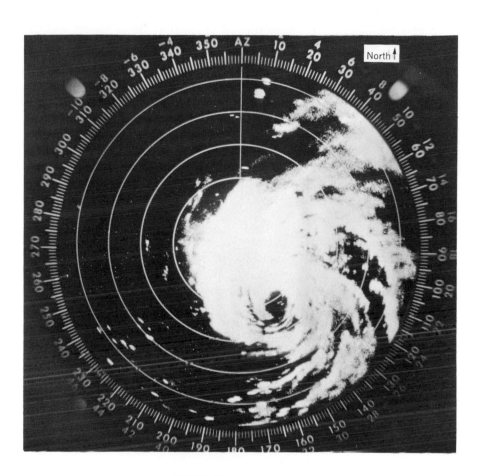

PLATE 11–6
PPI-scope picture of Hurricane Cleo taken with WSR-57
radar, Miami, Florida at 2245, August 26, 1964.
Radar has 100-nautical-mile range. Range circle intervals
are 20 nautical miles. Photo courtesy ESSA, Weather
Bureau.

Weather satellites have been a most useful addition to the arsenal of weather-reconnaissance "weapons." The cloud pictures taken by the Essa and Nimbus cameras have proved of great value in identifying the position and intensity of tropical storms, particularly when they lie outside the radar range. It is both interesting and instructive to compare radar and Tiros photographs of the same storm, Cleo, taken at (approximately) the same time. These are shown in Plates 11–5 and 11–6. Note particularly the spiral arms of squall lines which radiate in pinwheel fashion from the storm.

Each new instrument has its particular set of capabilities. Data gathered simultaneously by satellites, research aircraft, and radar will overlap somewhat, but supplement each other in a very useful manner.

There are three principal forecasting problems associated with hurricanes, which challenge the researcher. These deal with (a) genesis, (b) intensity, and (c) movement. Each of these is a very difficult problem about which much is known. However, in each case the *necessary* and *sufficient* conditions which govern the phenomenon and lead to accurate forecasting have not been sorted out. There is a fourth problem which is not a forecasting problem in the usual sense of the word. This deals with the whole unexplored area of storm modification. What, if anything, can be done to influence the future course of development of a particular storm? More will be said about this in the last chapter.

Progress in solving all four of these problems is directly related to the observation problem, for no theory can be put to the test in the absence of accurate description.

At the present time, theoreticians are attempting to construct mathematical models of the tropical storm which are adaptable to analysis by electronic computers. But the subjective-objective forecasts made by the "weatherman" still continue to be as good as or better than the completely objective forecasts issued by the computer from the numerical models so far developed. How long this will continue to be so is an intriguing question of our day.

CHAPTER 12

Problems of Modern Meteorology

And what of the future? The past 15 years have brought revolutionary changes to the field of meteorology. The activities in the field of weather modification by cloud seeding are but one minor aspect. The development of completely new observational methods (radar, weather satellites, high-altitude rockets, automatic-recording remote-readout weather stations, and so on) has provided the means of gathering masses of data from hitherto inaccessible regions in the atmosphere. The high-speed electronic computer has become available just in time to digest and analyze very rapidly the immense quantity of new data, which seems to increase exponentially year by year. The concept of meteorology has so broadened that the term "atmospheric science" is now more applicable. All kinds of scientists —electronics specialists, physicists, chemists, classical meteorologists, hydrologists, oceanographers, and mathematicians—are being rallied to bring their special skills to bear on the formidable problems of describing fully the state of the atmosphere and explaining the observed phenomena.

WEATHER MODIFICATION

Historians may agree that one of the most revolutionary thoughts to come out of the revolutionary 20th century was that weather control lay within man's capabilities. The thought was greatly stimulated by two discoveries made just before the middle of the century by two scientists, Vincent Schaefer and Bernard Vonnegut, who worked in the group headed by the great chemist, Irving Langmuir, of the General Electric Laboratories.

We have already seen, in the Bergeron process, that precipitation is initiated by the presence of ice crystals in an environment of supercooled water droplets. Because of the greater saturation vapor pressure over a water surface than over ice, evaporation of the droplets takes place, and the ice crystals grow as the evaporated water molecules find their way onto the ice surfaces.

Historical

Schaefer's discovery (July 1946) was that a cloud of supercooled water droplets formed in a deepfreeze could be transformed to an ice-crystal cloud by dropping small pellets of dry ice into this environment. Why should this happen? The temperature at which the solid carbon dioxide changes from a solid to a gaseous state (sublimes) is so low ($-78.5°C$) that the pellets cool the region through which they fall to temperatures below $-40°C$. It so happens that in cloud physics $-40°C$ is a "magic number," for this has been found to be the lowest temperature at which liquid water can exist in the atmosphere. Thus, in the region where the dry ice fell there would be many tiny ice crystals formed as a result of the low temperature. Other falling ice crystals, touching the surface of the small supercooled droplets, would infect (nucleate) them and initiate freezing. The water-hungry ice would soon acquire all the vapor released by the evaporating and freezing water droplets. In time the ice crystals would grow to such a size that they would fall to the bottom of the deepfreeze. The first field test of this discovery was made on November 13, 1946. Three pounds of crushed dry ice was dropped from an airplane along a three-mile track into a cloud deck of supercooled water droplets. Snow from the seeded cloud was observed to fall several thousand feet before it evaporated.

Vonnegut conceived the idea that if ice crystals could produce such a transformation in a supercooled cloud, it might be possible to obtain the same effect with a chemical closely resembling ice in its crystal structure. An intensive examination of the lattice constants of all crystals led to the identification of silver iodide as the closest match. Tests made in November 1946 showed that a silver iodide "smoke" produced by vaporizing an acetone solution of silver iodide in a flame did indeed produce the same effect when the temperature was less than $-5°C$.

The first field test of the effect of silver iodide as a seeding agent was carried out December 21, 1948. In this test a six-square-mile area of supercooled, thousand-foot-thick stratus cloud was transformed to ice crystals by seeding it from the air with lumps of burning charcoal impregnated with silver iodide.

These two discoveries, and the field tests, created a great flurry of excitement among members of the meteorological profession and among potential beneficiaries of cloud seeding: ranchers in areas of marginal rainfall, orchardists in hail-prone regions, and so on. It was possible to show that very large (10^{15}) numbers of silver iodide crystals resulted from the burning and subsequent recrystallization of one gram of silver iodide. Therefore it seemed very simple and logical to place ground-based silver-iodide generators upwind of the area to be seeded, and count on the air currents to waft the crystals upward to the levels at which there might be a deficiency of the natural ice crystals needed to initiate precipitation.

Meteorologists also hoped that massive overseeding of cumulus clouds that might develop into hail-producing thunderstorms could alter the development pattern in such a way as to thwart the buildup of hail.

The period between 1946 and 1950 was one of experimentation. The three armed services provided the General Electric investigators with support to carry on a five-year program of theoretical, laboratory, and field studies. This was known as Project Cirrus and it served as a springboard into the next era.

It so happened that a drought period had begun in 1946 in the southwestern United States and spread northeastward over the next 10 years. The combination of a pressing need for rain and a possible means of satisfying this need stimulated commercial cloud-seeding operations. These grew so rapidly that in 1952 more than one-tenth of the land area in the United States was under contract to be seeded. In addition to the commercial operations, the government-sponsored project called Artificial Cloud Nucleation (ACN) had been established as a follow-up to Project Cirrus. Everyone wondered whether cloud seeding would be effective in terms of measurable rainfall. Evaluations of the commercial cloud seeders (naturally) tended to be optimistic. Evaluations of the same projects carried out by impartial agencies were often much less so.

In 1953 the U.S. Advisory Committee on Weather Control was established. By this time it was obviously necessary to devise noncommercial experiments, from which the cloud seeder was under no obligation of making a dollar profit, in such a fashion that their evaluation would have the greatest possibility of showing convincing statistical evidence of the degree of success or failure of the seeding activity. Despite the most careful preplanning and use of randomization, the subsequent evaluations were incapable of determining the degree to which artificial seeding of the clouds modified the amount and type of precipitation.

By 1956 the first flush of enthusiasm had worn off. Consumers had been willing to take a risk on cloud seeding in the hope of making a large return on their relatively small investment. (For instance, if as little as an additional half inch of rain were caused by cloud seeding to fall on several hundred acres of wheat land at the right time, this could mean the difference between a good and a fair crop, which in terms of money could amount to tens of thousands of dollars.) After nearly a decade of unconvincing results, many groups who had been hiring the services of a commercial cloud seeder gave up their projects as too uncertain to warrant further investments. In 1956, commercial cloud seeding was reduced to about one-fourth of the 1952 peak, and has since remained at that level.

In response to the recognized need to enlarge our understanding of the physical causes of precipitation, most government research monies in the period since 1956 have been directed toward research activities in the broad area of cloud and atmospheric physics. This is undoubtedly a move in the proper direction.

Present Situation

The present situation of cloud seeding was summarized in an official statement (1957) issued by the American Meteorological Society, and little has since happened to produce any change:

1. The seeding of supercooled cloud with dry ice will usually convert at least a portion of the cloud to ice crystals. Under appropriate conditions such seeding may release variable amounts of precipitation from fairly deep and active cumulus clouds in which the natural release of precipitation has not already started. Small, inactive cumulus clouds are usually dissipated when they are seeded with dry ice. Holes or valleys may be produced in supercooled layer clouds or supercooled fogs by seeding them with dry ice.

2. The injection of water drops or hygroscopic salt particles into active, warm (nonsupercooled) cumulus clouds may release some rain. Small, inactive, warm cumulus may often be partially or completely dissipated by seeding them from above with water drops or other particles; such dissipation may occasionally be accompanied by the release of very light rain.

3. In some cases warm fog and stratus may be dissipated in restricted regions by the use of certain hygroscopic materials.

4. At temperatures below about −5°C, silver iodide crystals are known to affect supercooled clouds in much the same way as dry ice. The frequent absence of clear-cut results following the operation of ground-based silver iodide generators is believed to be due to one or more of the following causes: (a) the failure of the seeding materials to reach the supercooled clouds, (b) the absence of clouds that could be affected by seeding, (c) the decay of the silver iodide, (d) the presence of an ample supply of natural ice crystals, (e) topographical factors which defy quantitative measurement.

5. Cloud seeding acts only to trigger the release of precipitation from existing clouds. The release of substantial amounts of precipitation by either natural or artificial means requires the preexistence of an extensive moisture supply in the form of moist air currents and of active cloud-forming processes. For this reason the meteorological conditions most favorable for the artificial release of precipitation are very much the same as those which usually lead to the natural release of precipitation. This factor, plus the extreme natural variability of precipitation, makes the evaluation of the effects of seeding difficult and often inconclusive.

6. Evaluations performed by independent agencies have yielded reasonably convincing evidence of increases of precipitation due to the operation of ground-based silver iodide generators only for operations conducted in cold weather in regions where forced lifting of the air over a mountain range is an important factor. No convincing evidence has been presented which indicates that ground based silver iodide seeding affects the amount or character of the precipitation over flat country. This does not prove that there are no such effects but suggests that if present they are too small to be detected by statistical analyses of data available to this date.

7. In the absence of a truly quantitative theory of precipitation the best present means for obtaining a quantitative estimate of the effect of seeding on precipitation is through the statistical evaluation of randomized cloud-seeding experiments. The randomization is necessary to ensure valid interpretation of the results and a long series of such experiments may be necessary to detect small effects.

8. Present knowledge of atmospheric processes offers no real basis for the belief that the weather or climate of a large portion of the country can be significantly modified by cloud seeding. It is not intended to rule out the possibility of large-scale modifications of the weather at some future time, but it is believed that, if possible at all, this will require methods that alter the large-scale atmospheric circulations, possibly through changes in the radiation balance.

9. All cloud-seeding operations should be considered as experiments since the techniques are still under development and there is no sound basis for the quantitative estimation of the results in advance of the operation. As experiments they should be designed primarily to yield optimum scientific results. There is good reason to believe that improved returns from cloud seeding will result from a sound experimental approach and this should be fostered by all concerned.

Dry-Ice Seeding of Supercooled Fog

One of the wintertime hazards to aircraft operations is supercooled fog, which reduces visibilities below operating limits and disrupts regular airline schedules. Even though Schaefer's experiments had been widely known and accepted for a decade and a half, no organized program of airport weather improvement was established in the United States until 1963. Through an effort spearheaded by W. B. Beckwith of United Air Lines' department of meteorology, it has now been demonstrated that better than 80 percent success can be achieved in increasing visibility beyond the one-half mile landing limit. The method used is very simple. When fog forms at temperatures below 0°C prior to the time when an airliner is due to arrive, a light plane equipped with a supply of dry ice and nothing more complicated than a hand fertilizer spreader goes aloft. Then, as the pilot executes a racetrack pattern just on top of the cloud layer, crushed dry ice is dispersed through slots in the bottom of the aircraft. As it falls the dry ice produces tiny ice crystals which nucleate the supercooled water and produce a miniature snowstorm. The amount dispersed will vary from 50 to 600 pounds per flight, depending on circumstances. Visibility improvement usually occurs within 30 minutes after dispersal and lasts for an hour, which is sufficient time for the airliner to land, exchange passengers, refuel, and depart. This is an example of a weather-modification program in which direct economic gains are several times greater than the cost of the seeding operation. Not all airports are affected by wintertime supercooled fog. We may predict that those which are affected will find it advantageous to deal with the problem in the manner described.

Project Stormfury

Each year the coast of southeastern United States is menaced by one or more hurricanes which, if they come inland, cause billions of dollars of property damage and great human suffering. (We might add that these comments also apply to other geographic areas, such as the east coast of Asia and Australia.) Motivated by this fact, the U.S. Weather Bureau and the U.S. Navy established in 1962 an interagency cooperative project called Project Stormfury under the direction of Dr. Joanne Simpson.

Project Stormfury is an experiment in hurricane modification by cloud seeding. The seeding agent is silver iodide dispersed from pyrotechnic bomb generators released from aircraft. This method of delivery makes it possible to seed a large area of a supercooled cloud tower massively and simultaneously over a large volume in space.

The purpose of seeding in this experiment is not to make rain; it is to produce a change in the dynamic structure of the storm by the sudden release of latent heat energy which results when the water cloud is changed to ice. The theoreticians of the project expect from their calculations that the clouds in the eye wall should move outward with a reduction in maximum wind speed.

In 1963 project personnel carried out a complicated two-day seeding operation of the eye wall of hurricane Beulah. This involved very sophisticated logistics such as coordinating specially equipped aircraft. Three were deployed to make detailed measurements of the core structure in terms of wind speed, air pressure, temperature, humidity, liquid water content, number of freezing nuclei, and cloud form. These measurements were taken from two hours prior to seeding to two hours after seeding. One low-flying B 26 made cloud studies. One plane circled the eye wall and dropped instruments by parachute to measure air pressure near the eye. Two high-flying planes photographed the storm from above. All planes were directed from a Super Constellation "command post."

No seeding was done in 1964. The entire year was used to evaluate data from the 1963 project, and to prepare for more sophisticated experimentation in 1965 and later. Was the 1963 project successful? No simple answer was expected and we will not attempt to give one. (Dr. Simpson's interesting report is to be found in *Scientific American*, December, 1964.) It is known that the hurricane is a storm subject to some precarious balance of forces—witness the erratic tracks sometimes followed. In such circumstances it is very difficult to sort out, with certainty, what happened as a direct result of the cloud seeding. The view of the project leaders is that it is quite possible their hypothesis will be verified. If, on the other hand, it is disproved, something new and therefore of value will have been learned about hurricanes. The new knowledge can then be incorporated in the revised hypothesis. This is the way science continues to advance.

DATA ACQUISITION BY RADAR AND SATELLITE

Radar

Perhaps the question has arisen: If radar can identify precipitation, can it be used as a substitute for a rain gage? It is well known that isohyetal (lines of equal rainfall) maps are limited in their accuracy by the wide spacing of the rain gages and the terrain of the land. In principle, a radar system of monitoring rainfall amounts could be more accurate. In practice, however, the problems of working out a good system are not yet solved, because of financial and theoretical problems. One method now in use employs a long-exposure camera to record the echoes on the PPI-scope over a period of time. The film density is measured with a densitometer and this reading is related to the intensity of the echo-producing rainfall. Then plots of film density and range are calibrated according to the equivalent rainfall in inches. At the present time there are still some important problems to be solved. However, we can anticipate that in the future radar measurements of precipitation may be supplemented by the rain-gage net, rather than vice versa, as at present.

For many years astronomers have made use of the *Doppler principle* in studying the motion of distant stars. The basis of this principle is that if a star is approaching the earth its light will appear to be very slightly "bluer" than it would be were there no relative motion, and if it is receding its light will be a bit "redder." The Doppler principle also explains why the pitch of a train whistle sounds higher than normal as the train approaches the listener standing at the crossing, and lower as it recedes.

Within the past 10 years or so, weather research scientists have seen the potentialities of using radar data in such a way that Doppler analyses could be made from it. In what sense would this yield valuable data? As we have seen in the section on hail, an accurate hail forecast requires accurate information on the size distribution of drops and the strengths of the vertical currents in the cumulonimbus cloud. Each moving drop illuminated by radar energy becomes a secondary source of radiation which is returned to the radar receiver. Therefore, in principle, the relative particle motion within the cloud should be revealed by Doppler analysis, if the data are properly displayed.

To this end, engineers have designed and produced Doppler radars which are now in experimental use in many cloud-physics research centers, and increasing numbers of technical reports on the subject are appearing in scientific journals. It is too early to assess the potentialities of this technique. However, despite its technical difficulty, there seems to be general optimism that, in the future, Doppler radar may be one of the cloud physicist's most useful tools.

Weather Satellite

Another milestone was reached when on August 28, 1964, meteorological satellite Nimbus I was launched from Vandenberg Air Force Base, California. The efficiency of this satellite was reduced by a malfunction which prevented it from attaining a circular orbit at 900 kilometers.

Nevertheless, night and day cloud-cover photographs have been obtained over 50–75 percent of the world on a daily basis. Each of the cameras has a field of view of 35 degrees, and together they cover a field from horizon to horizon perpendicular to the track of the satellite. One of the significant improvements over the Tiros series is the High Resolution Infrared Scanning Radiometer. This senses the terrestrial radiation emitted in the narrow "window" between 3.6 and 4.2 microns. Nighttime cloud-cover pictures have been taken with a quality comparable to that of the Tiros vidicon pictures.

The most immediate practical benefit from the meteorological satellite is its ability to provide advance warning of severe storms. This is particularly important in the case of storms which develop over data-sparse areas contiguous to regions of high population density such as Japan, Southeast Asia, and Central America.

One may estimate conservatively that the potential saving in property in the United States by improved advance storm warnings will exceed by several orders of magnitude the total cost of the meteorological-satellite program. The saving would be even greater in more critical areas like those just mentioned.

All forms of transportation—air, sea, and surface—will continue to benefit from the meteorological-satellite program. Ships will be warned of tropical storms in regions of sparse data, so that appropriate changes in course may be taken. The ability of the satellite to photograph regions of surface ice at sea will allow more efficient routing of ships which ply arctic or antarctic waters. Aircraft may be routed around severe-weather areas which have not been spotted on synoptic weather charts. This will be of particular value to aircraft on long over-water flights. As an example, flight missions between American bases in Antarctica and New Zealand, a region in which surface-weather information is notoriously sparse, will now, as the result of the use of weather satellites, have advance notice of developing storm situations.

Military operations are particularly dependent on the weather factor. Thus the information that satellites can supply concerning the weather in data-sparse ocean and land areas will be of inestimable importance in time of war.

One of the nonmeteorological applications of satellite observations is the detection of large locust swarms such as occur occasionally in Eastern Africa. Since some swarms cover as much as 50 square miles, they might be seen by the satellite cameras. If the swarm were in an unpopulated area, such an observation might give sufficient warning time to rush insecticides by plane and destroy the swarm before it reached agricultural areas.

DATA ASSIMILATION

Sometimes it seems odd that in this age of nuclear fusion, forecasts which are 90 percent accurate cannot be made more than 48 hours in advance. Why should this be so? The reason is really very straightforward. The atmosphere is an *extremely* complex system, and our understanding of it as a system is still woefully incomplete. We are well beyond the kindergarten stage, but we are far from having attained our Ph.D. degree. Perhaps we are "about to enter high school." Even at this level, it is clear in outline what must be done if we are to achieve the full understanding that is so necessary. As in other sciences, for example nuclear physics, accurate and complete description leads to workable models, and application of the data to the models leads to accurate prediction. These steps must precede successful efforts to control the weather.

We must achieve a weather system which is literally global in extent. This is a task of staggering dimensions. Yet it is well within our technological capabilities at the present time, even though one cannot be so optimistic about our present political and managerial capabilities.

This weather system will make use of the whole arsenal of instruments for gathering the data necessary to describe the global three-dimensional atmosphere. It will expand the present network of surface stations by increased use of automatic remote-readout stations located in the oceans and in strategic but unpopulated land areas. More rawinsondes, transosondes, and meteorological rockets will be employed to probe the vertical dimension of the atmosphere. And Nimbus-Essa satellites will look down on the atmosphere in increasing numbers. No single instrument is sufficient by itself. Each complements the other by providing a type of information the other is incapable of measuring. Of all the new approaches to data gathering, the meteorological satellite is likely to have the most revolutionary effect on forecasting. Here we are presented with the opportunity of having, within a few years, earthwide observations of cloud cover, outgoing terrestrial radiation, and perhaps even incoming solar radiation, on a routine day-to-day basis.

Even at this moment scientists are grappling with two problems which must be solved if the weather-satellite program is to fulfill its expectations. The first has to do with the mechanics of handling the enormous masses of data which pour earthward. To describe a complete Northern-Hemisphere surface map at present, it is necessary to feed some 10,000 bits of information in binary language into a digital computer. In contrast a single picture from an Essa satellite contains 10,000,000 bits. It is estimated that in 1975 the meteorological-satellite network will be generating 10,000,000,000 bits per day! Because of the vast increase in the number of data, better code language for handling, disseminating, and storing this information must be developed. And since the present limitations of a global weather system are primarily limitations of economy, not of technology, we have reason to be confident that these improvements can be made.

The second problem has to do with the interpretation of the data. One atmospheric scientist, Myron Ligda, suggests that the situation resembles that of a group of paleontologists who have discovered a new bed of fossils. Their first task is to dig, recover, and catalog. The second, which must follow the first, is to study, assemble, and interpret. At present the emphasis in satellite meteorology is upon the recovery and cataloguing stages. A few interpretations of the simplest and most obvious facts have been made about tropical revolving storms and their appearance from above. But forecasters would like to relate areas of cloud cover to precipitation, cloud patterns to circulation intensities, radiation to the complex patterns of heat exchange taking place between ground, ocean, and atmosphere. A time interval of years, and perhaps decades, will have to elapse before these more subtle interpretations can be made.

A new machine, now being developed, may turn out to be extremely useful in the interpretation of satellite information. This is the pattern-recognition machine, which is sometimes called a learning machine. Such a machine can be trained to recognize patterns (such as those of clouds and infrared radiation) and associate them with events correlated with the patterns. This technique is now used in a crude and limited fashion in forecasting, often without benefit of machines. It is called forecasting by *analog*. The forecaster looks at a number of previous weather maps, finds a series which resembles most closely the present one, and forecasts the future from what happened in the past. Since a computer can store a very large number of complex situations in its memory, and scan through *all* of them in a short period of time, this technique could be very fruitful in conjunction with satellite information.

Many new and exciting problems for research present themselves. One is the new insight into the basic structure of cyclonic storms provided by both radar and satellite. Both have shown that precipitation is associated with spiral arms which radiate from the storm in pinwheel fashion. In this pattern, fronts are but major spiral arms which coincide with air-mass boundaries. Much valuable information leading to more accurate forecasts of precipitation will come from further investigations. The preceding comments lead us to some observations as to why progress must be made on the meteorological front.

WATER SUPPLY AND AIR POLLUTION

Two of man's most important natural resources are pure water and clean air. Both are essential to life itself. In the United States both have been largely taken for granted, until recently. Though the Southwest is somewhat of an exception, the majority of the 50 states usually receive adequate rainfall to fill the needs of their residents. It comes as a shock to be told that we are now living in the beginning of an era when pure water may be in short supply.

The water demands resulting from the population explosion are already creating tensions between regions which have an overabundance and those which do not have enough to satisfy the rapidly increasing needs of their growing population. This tension has been felt for some number of years between the water-hungry states of California and Arizona over rights to the water of the Colorado River. They are beginning to be felt between California and the Pacific Northwest States as California looks abroad for more and more water.

It is still too early to predict with any degree of confidence what may be done, through the exercise of weather control, to bring about a more equitable geographical distribution of rain. A comment made by Tor Bergeron, an eminent meteorologist, in an address prepared for the 1965 International Conference on Cloud Physics, Tokyo, illustrates at least one of the possibilities:

> As a good example of what can (or could) be done along such lines, let me first mention a striking suggestion put forth independently by E. G. Bowen and H. Weickmann. They have both pointed out that by overseeding the onshore air flow with condensation nuclei along a coast with a pronounced rain maximum, this maximum might be shifted somewhat inland, to the mutual benefit of a too rainy coastal strip and the arid interior of the country. Such an overseeding could raise the number of cloud elements by several orders of magnitude in the coastal oreigenic cloud system, and diminish the size of the droplets correspondingly, thereby impeding the coalescence in this "warm" cloud. Consequently, more of the water content in the onshore flow would be kept for precipitation further inland, and generally at a higher level, where it often is bitterly needed, and where natural or artificially injected ice-nuclei then might perform a better precipitation release than would otherwise be the case.
>
> In my opinion, this approach is a very fruitful one. Moreover, additional seeding with ice-nuclei in the inland orographic clouds would probably form one of the few instances where such seeding can be expected to become efficient. Before trying the above project in the field, at the meso- and macroscale, though, its chances should be tested (a) by synoptic-statistical studies in suitable coastal regions (S.E. Australia, S.W. Norway, N.W.

Oregon) as to the occurrence of "warm" clouds with considerable rain in the coastal range, (b) by numerical experiments concerning the effect at the micro- and macroscale of the named overseeding.

The majority of the citizens of the United States breathe air which is relatively clean. Because of man's inclination to use the atmosphere as a vast dump into which to pour the waste products of industrial and urban combustion, to say nothing of fissionable by-products of atomic explosions, pure air for urban dwellers may be the exception rather than the rule.

Whereas the problem of redistribution of water resources is one which exists within the boundaries of national states (though we grant that this problem has international dimensions as well), the atmosphere has no regard for such boundaries. Americans breathe the same air which at an earlier time was breathed (and contaminated) by the Chinese, Japanese, Canadians, and Cubans. Our point here is simply that every citizen in every country has a stake in whatever efforts are made to manage or manipulate the atmosphere.

A global weather system by its very nature must involve cooperative participation by all nations at a political level as well as at a scientific level. The World Meteorological Organization is a very large step taken in the direction of cooperation at both levels. Perhaps it will be through the agency of the WMO that the problems of joint surveillance of the atmosphere and joint communication and processing of meteorological data may be attacked with the greatest hope for success.

We may predict with high confidence that the world society of the future will become increasingly complex, increasingly highly organized, *and* increasingly interdependent. Perhaps cooperation at the meteorological level, directed to the betterment of living conditions for all, will be an example for those other forms of cooperation which are a prerequisite for survival of the human race.

APPENDIX

1. *Notation using powers of* 10

$$1000 = 10 \times 10 \times 10 = 10^3$$
$$100 = 10 \times 10 \qquad = 10^2$$
$$10 = 10 \qquad\qquad = 10^1$$
$$1 = \ 1 \qquad\qquad = 10^0$$
$$0.1 = \frac{1}{10} \qquad\qquad = 10^{-1}$$
$$0.01 = \frac{1}{10 \times 10} \qquad = 10^{-2}$$
$$0.001 = \frac{1}{10 \times 10 \times 10} = 10^{-3}$$

2. *Metric units of length*

10^3	kilometer (km)
10^2	
10^1	
$1 = 10^0$	meter (m)
10^{-1}	
10^{-2}	centimeter (cm)
10^{-3}	millimeter (mm)
10^{-4}	
10^{-5}	
10^{-6}	micron (μ)
10^{-10}	angstrom (A)

$$1 \text{ km} = 0.62 \text{ mi}$$
$$1 \text{ m} = 3.28 \text{ ft}$$
$$2.54 \text{ cm} = 1 \text{ in.}$$

3. *Metric units of mass*

10^3	kilogram (kg)
$1 = 10^0$	gram (g)
10^{-3}	milligram (mg)

$$1 \text{ kg} = 2.2 \text{ lb}$$
$$454 \text{ g} = 1 \text{ lb}$$

4. *Temperature*

Centigrade (°C)	Kelvin (°K)	Fahrenheit (°F)	
100	373	212	←Boiling
0	273	32	←Freezing
		0	
−40	233	−40	
−273	−0		←Absolute zero
(Not to scale)			

$$°C = (°F - 32) \times \tfrac{5}{9}$$
$$°F = °C \times \tfrac{9}{5} + 32$$
$$(9°F = 5°C)$$

5. *Trigonometry*

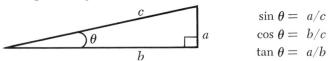

$$\sin \theta = a/c$$
$$\cos \theta = b/c$$
$$\tan \theta = a/b$$

6. *Greek alphabet*

α	alpha	ι	iota	ρ	rho
β	beta	κ	kappa	σ	sigma
γ	gamma	λ	lambda	τ	tau
δ	delta	μ	mu	υ	upsilon
ϵ	epsilon	ν	nu	ϕ	phi
ζ	zeta	ξ	xi	χ	chi
η	eta	o	omicron	ψ	psi
θ	theta	π	pi	ω	omega

7. *Physical quantities, defining equations, and units*

	mks	fps
Length h, z, L, l	meter	foot
Mass m	kilogram	slug
Force F	newton	pound-force
Work $W = F \cdot s$	joule	foot-pound
Kinetic energy $KE = \tfrac{1}{2}m\, v^2$	joule	foot-pound
Potential energy $PE = mgh$	joule	foot-pound
Power $P = W/t$	watt	horsepower
Charge Q	coulomb	
Current $I = Q/t$	ampere	
Potential $V = W/Q$	volt	
Capacitance $C = Q/V$	farad	

8. *Pressure, standard atmosphere, sea level (conversions)*
   14.7 lb/in^2 = 1013.2 mb = 1,013,200 dynes/cm^2 = 760 mm of Hg

9. *Velocity (conversions)*
   10 mph = 8.69 knots = 16.09 km/hr = 4.47 m/sec = 14.67 ft/sec

NAME INDEX

SUBJECT INDEX